EDUCATORS GUIDE TO FREE SCIENCE MATERIALS

*

Edited by
Kathleen Suttles Nehmer

*

Educational Consultant
Michael Belongie, B. S.
Curriculum Manager, Randolph Public Schools

*

FIFTY-FIRST ANNUAL EDITION
2010-2011

(For use during school year 2010-2011)

D1511339

EDUCATORS PROGRESS SERVICE, INC.
214 Center Street
Randolph, Wisconsin 53956

Published by

Educators Progress Service, Inc.

Randolph, Wisconsin 53956

Library of Congress Catalog Card Number 61-919

Printed and Bound in the United States of America

International Standard Book Number 978-0-87708-505-8

Publisher's note:

Inside this Guide you will find materials regarding creationism as well as evolution. These are listed
in the interest of science only. Different people believe in different things and it is our intention to
provide listings of materials for all disciplines if those materials exist. I would like it to be known,
however, that my own personal belief is in the Divine Creator, our one and only Father in Heaven.

TABLE OF CONTENTS

    Know the title of the material you want? These
    pages will help you find it.

III

IV

FROM THE PUBLISHER'S DESK

Science is something we can actually SEE all around us everyday. From the sunny day (or thunderstorm) that greets us as we rise, to the breakfast we consume, to the transportation we take to get to work or school and back home again–these are all examples of science. Understanding how each of these things work is a large part of science–and this understanding leads us to produce better items to do these same jobs. (Okay, maybe we can't do much about the weather but everyday we are seeing science produce more accurate forecasts so we at least know what we can expect). Science is an ever changing field and school textbooks cannot keep up with this constantly developing area. Thus, supplementary teaching aids have become a necessity.

This 50th annual edition of EDUCATORS GUIDE TO FREE SCIENCE MATERIALS tells you where to find these teaching aids for your classroom, free of charge–**all materials listed are new this year**. As you might imagine, the process of revising the annual editions of the EDUCATORS GUIDES is a time consuming process (there are now eighteen titles in the series). In our efforts to find new materials every year, we write thousands of letters to companies inquiring about materials they are willing to offer free to educators and others. Each and every year these letters are written. If no response is received, no materials from that source are included. **No materials are included if we have not received permission from the sponsor to tell you about their availability**. All addresses are verified as well. Your requests for FREE educational aids WILL BE ANSWERED.

It's a lot of work but it is very rewarding. It really is a pleasure to be able to point educators to teaching aids that not only **save tight budgets** but **add to the educational environment**. We like to find materials that "help teachers teach," not only to make their jobs easier but to help students learn more.

It is fortunate, for students and educators alike, that the availability and quality of free supplementary teaching aids increases annually. It is imperative that teachers are able to "handle what's thrown at them" in a timely manner–these materials provide the ability to help you do so. Any comments you may have regarding this GUIDE are welcomed–we like to learn from you, too.

Kathy

Kathy Nehmer

P. S. **Be sure to use only the 2010-2011 GUIDE for the current school year**, as hundreds of titles available last year are no longer available!

HOW TO USE THE EDUCATORS GUIDE TO FREE SCIENCE MATERIALS

The 2010-2011 GUIDE provides busy (and cash-strapped) educators with information about 777 free videotapes, films, filmstrips, lesson plans, slides, print materials, and web resources to help save money and enrich the classroom. Finding the materials you desire, and requesting them, is easy.

The **BODY** of the GUIDE (white pages) gives you full information on each of the 777 titles, **ALL of which are new in this edition**. These 777 new titles dramatically illustrate one reason that it is so important to use only the most current edition of the GUIDE.

 If you are in need of helpful teaching materials within minutes you'll find the mouse icon (shown at the left) to be very useful. All Internet resources (lesson plans, web sites, downloadable articles, WebQuests, etc). are clearly indicated within the body of the book with this icon. Just enter the URL and you will instantly access the FREE teaching aid you need!

The **TITLE INDEX** (blue pages) is an alphabetical listing of all items appearing in the body of the GUIDE, with page references. This enables readers to locate any item whose title is known. The TITLE INDEX guides you directly to any specific item in the GUIDE, where you can read the description of the material and find all ordering information.

In the **SUBJECT INDEX** (yellow pages) all materials relating to topics of a more specific nature than the general subject headings in the body of the GUIDE are categorized. These "yellow pages" work like the familiar "yellow pages" of a telephone directory.

The **SOURCE INDEX** (green pages) provides an alphabetical list of the names of the 380 organizations from which materials can be obtained. Also included in each entry are page numbers which indicate where the materials from that particular source appear in the body of the GUIDE. Use of this feature facilitates the ordering, with one letter, of more than one selection if a source offers several.

ANALYSIS OF EDUCATORS GUIDE TO FREE
SCIENCE MATERIALS–2010

	TOTAL ITEMS
Chemistry	22
Conservation Education	153
Earth and Space Science	156
General Science	99
Life Science	80
Nature Study	137
Physical Science	40
Teacher Reference	<u>90</u>
TOTALS	777

These numbers represent 4 sets of slides, 282 videotapes, 57 print materials, and 434 computer resources–**ALL OF WHICH ARE NEW IN THIS EDITION.**

YOUR LETTERS OF REQUEST

When requesting materials, please make your letter of request clear. Identify yourself and your organization. Be sure to use any identifying numbers provided and **observe any restrictions** on distribution as indicated in the GUIDE.

Do not be alarmed if everything you request does not come. The list of materials changes; materials go out of date and are replaced by new items. We cannot tell at the time of printing how long each item will last. Sponsors are asked to assure us, with reasonable certainty, that their materials will be available for approximately one year. It is to meet this need that the GUIDE is revised annually.

There are 380 sources of free materials listed in the **2010-2011 EDUCATORS GUIDE TO FREE SCIENCE MATERIALS.** Please make certain that the request you are making is to the proper company.

In writing for materials, the following form is suggested. The listing used as an example is selected from page 8.

REGIONAL SCHOOL #7
Central Avenue
Winstead, Connecticut 06098

August 8, 2010

The Forest Foundation
853 Lincoln Way, Suite 104
Auburn, CA 85603

Dear Sponsor:

We would like to borrow the following videotape as listed in the 2010 EDUCATORS GUIDE TO FREE SCIENCE MATERIALS:

California's Changing Forest: A Case for Management

We would like to view the vide on September 10, 2010. A satisfactory alternate date is September 17. Thank you for your cooperation in assisting us to enrich the curriculum of our school.

Sincerely,

Rick DeJager
Elementary Science

HOW TO COOPERATE WITH THE SPONSORS

Subscribers to EPS services have frequently asked us for guidelines to follow in requesting sponsored materials. The following 14 questions are quoted from an address given by Thomas J. Sinclair, Ph.D., formerly Manager of Educational and Group Relations for the Association of American Railroads, at a convention of the National Science Teachers Association.

1. Poor handwriting, which you strive to correct in your pupils, often makes coupons and other requests useless. Is your handwriting distinct on requests?

2. Neither industry nor the U. S. Postal Service is omniscient. Do you include complete and accurate details of your address, including zip number?

3. Postcards, small social stationery, or slips of paper present filing problems and can easily be lost. Do you use standard sized stationery?

4. Remember that in big companies thousands of pieces of mail go in and out every day. Do you allow sufficient time for handling your request.

5. Most students advise businesses that they are <u>studing</u> a topic. Do you check your spelling?

6. If you were on the receiving end, you'd have a different view of mass classroom letter-writing projects to the same business organization. Do you make certain that only one request goes to a particular source from your classroom?

7. Instructions on a coupon, in a guide, or on an order form are there for a purpose. Do you read and follow these instructions?

8. Some organizations have dozens–sometimes hundreds–of different teaching aids. Specific needs should be outlined. Do you say "Send me everything you've got" or its equivalent?

9. Source lists and guides get out of date. Do you check to see if the list you are consulting is a recent one?

10. Sometimes aids are in limited supply or available only to teachers in single copies. Do you keep requests reasonable and show some respect for the costs of materials?

11. Sample copies are for examination, with the privilege of ordering quantities subsequently. Do you order classroom quantities blind–without first examining an item for suitability for your purpose?

12. Companies keep records and files. They frequently like to know precisely where their materials are going. Are you careful to mention your school connection?

13. Do you make a real effort to make certain the organization you are writing to is the correct one, and that it could reasonably have the material you are seeking?

14. Duplications and unnecessary correspondence only slow good service to the teaching profession. Do you consult your associates to see whether needed materials have already been supplied to your school?

These questions provide specific suggestions that should, in the long run, make for happier sponsors and better service to educators.

EVALUATION OF INDUSTRY-SPONSORED EDUCATIONAL MATERIALS

The business community has long recognized its obligation to support the agencies of the community that contribute to its security and well-being. In partial fulfillment of this obligation, industry trade associations and non-profit organizations have been producing supplementary materials for use in our nation's schools for some time. Properly planned, sponsored educational resources serve a valuable role and are particularly effective in giving information to students in an area where the sponsoring organization has achieved a high degree of specialization. When properly designed, sponsored materials can be used to motivate students and direct their energies into productive channels of growth.

Educational systems can respond more effectively to changes in technology, job structure, income, population, and manpower requirements with close support and involvement of industry. Both sectors have a common goal of strengthening the institutional programs at all levels in our schools. Operationally, this requires a strong industry-education alliance, particularly at the local level in preparing people for a productive role in the marketplace.

The National Association for Industry-Education Cooperation (NAIEC) was established in 1964 as a logical development out of the Business Industry Section of the National Science Teachers Association. Its purposes were (and still are) to bring about a better understanding between Education and the Business community and to mobilize the resources of education and industry to improve the relevance and quality of educational programs at all levels.

NAIEC members represent a variety of private and public organizations. Major trade associations, corporations, schools, and school districts are members. School superintendents, college presidents, curriculum and other education coordinators, business executives, industry-education coordinators, deans, department chairpersons, career education and job placement specialists, and faculty participate in the Association's programs.

The membership works together to identify problems of mutual interest, formulate plans and procedures, develop acceptable business-sponsored instructional materials, and communicate the advantages of industry-education cooperation.

The NAIEC membership has determined that the set of guiding principles (see below) for the preparation of materials for distribution to schools established by a study financed by American Iron and Steel Institute and carried out by the George Peabody Teachers College are valid and has found that materials embracing these criteria have usually found acceptance and use in the nation's schools and classrooms.

1. Work with a representative group of teachers and administrators to ensure meeting a curricular need.

2. Provide factual material desired by the schools. Include only that information which is significant to the study of particular problems or topics of concern to the teacher and student.

3. Exclude all advertising. A credit line naming the sponsor is enough; indeed schools need to know the publisher and the date of the material.

4. Materials must be written to the particular age level, reading level, interests, and maturity of the group for whom they are intended.

5. Keep the materials free of persuasion; avoid special pleading of the interests of any one point of view or group.

6. Make the materials available to educators only upon request.

X

In 1976 members of the NAIEC developed "A Guide for Evaluating Industry-Sponsored Educational Materials" which embodies the above listed criteria from the educator's viewpoint. This guide is an effort by the National Association for Industry-Education Cooperation (NAIEC) to present teachers with an instrument for evaluating sponsored education resources. These supplemental materials may take the form of teacher guides, filmstrips, games actually designed for the classroom, or pamphlets, reprinted articles, annual reports which may provide valuable background information but are not developed specifically for the teacher's use. (It is suggested that the Guide is more effective with the items actually designed for the classroom.)

If, after completing your evaluation of those items designed for the classroom, you have no further use for the instrument, the sponsoring organization providing the item would appreciate your evaluation with any comments you might have for guidance in the development of future materials. Hopefully this will foster closer industry-education cooperation.

A GUIDE FOR EVALUATING INDUSTRY-SPONSORED EDUCATIONAL MATERIALS

Title of material _____ Date produced, if available _____

Sponsor (name of organization)_____

Type of material: Audio _____ Audiovisual _____ Printed _____ Other _____

Type of instruction suitable for this material: Individual _____ Group _____

This evaluation is based on usage in _____ (grade level)

Evaluator _____ Date _____

Subject area/School _____

Address _____

_____

INSTRUCTIONS FOR USE:

Use the following scale by evaluating the material as it relates to your situation. Each of the descriptive statements is followed by a scale of (1), (2), (3), (4), (5). Indicate your assessment of the material by circling the appropriate number in the scale:

(1) Definitely yes   (4) Definitely no
(2) Yes   (5) Material cannot be evaluated on this concept
(3) No

OBJECTIVES

Identified outcomes may be obtained through use of the material.

1 2 3 4 5

The materials are representative of the curriculum involved; that is, they help further the objectives of the curriculum.

1 2 3 4 5

ABILITY RANGE

The materials provide for the range of abilities and aptitudes of all pupils.

1 2 3 4 5

CONTENT

The material is contemporary.

1 2 3 4 5

The material is controversial.

1 2 3 4 5

The material presents alternative views.

1 2 3 4 5

The material does not present a bias for a product, organization, or social cause.

1 2 3 4 5

The material does present a bias for a product, organization, or social cause.

1 2 3 4 5

If such a bias exists, it does not invalidate the material for my purposes.

1 2 3 4 5

The nature and scope of the material content is adequate to meet curriculum objectives.

1 2 3 4 5

The material is supplementary to the curriculum.

1 2 3 4 5

The material offers opportunity for integration of the subject within the existing curriculum.

1 2 3 4 5

The material correlates with a specific discipline area.

1 2 3 4 5

The material introduces experiences that would not otherwise be available in the classroom.

1 2 3 4 5

The material suggests other resources, supplementary and/or instructional.

1 2 3 4 5

XII

UTILIZATION CHARACTERISTICS

SCALE

The anticipated time utilization is commensurate with anticipated value of outcome.

1 2 3 4 5

The material demands special conditions for use.

1 2 3 4 5

The material is appropriate for student's reading level.

1 2 3 4 5

The material is appropriate for student's interest level.

1 2 3 4 5

The material is attractive to students.

1 2 3 4 5

The material provides motivation for students.

1 2 3 4 5

PRESENTATION OF MATERIALS

Provisions are made for evaluating the material as it is used within the educational program.

1 2 3 4 5

Instructional procedures are outlined.

1 2 3 4 5

The style of the presentation is likely to lead students toward accomplishing basic goals.

1 2 3 4 5

Sample student activities and questions are included.

1 2 3 4 5

The instructions to teachers are clearly stated.

1 2 3 4 5

The intended use is easily understood.

1 2 3 4 5

The production quality of the materials is acceptable.

1 2 3 4 5

EVALUATION

The material provides for feedback to the user.

1 2 3 4 5

The material provides for self-evaluation.

1 2 3 4 5

XIII

Atomic ThinkQuest Team
Learn about chemistry.

Availability:	All requesters
Suggested Grade:	6-12
Order Number:	not applicable
Format:	Web Site
Special Notes:	This URL will lead you to a subject page. Then click on the appropriate subject heading.

Source: ThinkQuest
World Wide Web URL:
http://www.thinkquest.org/pls/html/think.library

Chemical Changes
Students will learn about matter and the chemical changes it undergoes.

Availability:	All requesters
Suggested Grade:	9-12
Order Number:	not applicable
Format:	Online Lesson Plan

Source: K. Matthie
World Wide Web URL:
http://teachertech.rice.edu/Participants/kmatthie/
lessons/chemicalchanges/index.html

Chemistry Behind Cooking WebQuest
Learn how chemistry is involved in cooking.

Availability:	All requesters
Suggested Grade:	9-12
Order Number:	not applicable
Format:	WebQuest

Source: Mrs. K. Shimp
World Wide Web URL:
http://chsweb.lr.k12.nj.us/kshimp/cooking/
chemwebquest.htm

Chemistry of Castor Oil and Its Derivatives and Their Applications, The
A technical summary of castor oil reactions with extensive information on uses and applications of this unique industrial oil.

Availability:	Single copies to schools, libraries, and homeschoolers in the United States and Canada. Make request on official stationery.
Suggested Grade:	9-Adult
Order Number:	order by title
Format:	Bulletin

Source: International Castor Oil Association, The
24 Burton Avenue
Woodmere, NY 11598
Fax: 1-516-569-6940
Email Address: icoa@icoa.org

Chemmybear
Offers a sort of tool kit for chemistry teachers.

Availability:	All requesters
Suggested Grade:	9-12
Order Number:	not applicable
Format:	Web Site

Source: Paul Groves
World Wide Web URL: http://www.chemmybear.com/

Chempire
Site designed for students and teachers of high school chemistry to be used to review material for a test or lab.

Availability:	All requesters
Suggested Grade:	9-Adult
Order Number:	not applicable
Format:	Web Site
Special Notes:	This URL will lead you to a subject page. Then click on the appropriate subject heading.

Source: ThinkQuest
World Wide Web URL:
http://www.thinkquest.org/pls/html/think.library

ChemWeb Online
Easy-to-navigate site if you need to study for a chemistry exam.

Availability:	All requesters
Suggested Grade:	9-12
Order Number:	not applicable
Format:	Web Site
Special Notes:	This URL will lead you to a subject page. Then click on the appropriate subject heading.

Source: ThinkQuest
World Wide Web URL:
http://www.thinkquest.org/pls/html/think.library

Creative Chemistry
Worksheets, teaching notes, puzzles, quizzes, and much more for learning chemistry.

Availability:	All requesters
Suggested Grade:	9-12
Order Number:	not applicable
Format:	Web Site

Source: Nigel Saunders
World Wide Web URL: http://www.creative-
chemistry.org.uk/index.htm

CyberChemistry at Your Fingertips
Four simple experiments to try at home (with parental supervision), using items commonly found in the house.

Availability:	All requesters
Suggested Grade:	9-12
Order Number:	not applicable
Format:	Web Site
Special Notes:	This URL will lead you to a subject page. Then click on the appropriate subject heading.

Source: ThinkQuest
World Wide Web URL:
http://www.thinkquest.org/pls/html/think.library

Digital Chemistry Textbook
Covers gases, chemical reactions, liquids, solids, and other basic topics. Advanced placement chemistry students will find this useful.

 Indicates an Internet Resource--just enter the URL and instantly access the FREE teaching aid you need!
All materials listed in this 2010-2011 edition are BRAND NEW!

1

Availability: All requesters
Suggested Grade: 9-12
Order Number: not applicable
Format: Web Site
Special Notes: This URL will lead you to a subject page. Then click on the appropriate subject heading.
Source: ThinkQuest
World Wide Web URL:
http://www.thinkquest.org/pls/html/think.library

Flame in the Chemistry Lab

Tests the heat zones of a Bunsen burner and shows some elements' coloration when placed in the flame. Notes that chemistry is everywhere.

Availability: Schools, libraries, and homeschoolers in the United States who serve the hearing impaired.
Suggested Grade: 10-Adult
Order Number: 11031
Production Date: 2001
Format: DVD
Special Notes: Also available as live streaming video over the Internet.
Terms: Sponsor pays all transportation costs. Return one week after receipt. Participation is limited to deaf or hard of hearing Americans, their parents, families, teachers, counselors, or others whose use would benefit a deaf or hard of hearing person. Only one person in the audience needs to be hearing impaired. You must register--which is free. These videos are all open-captioned--no special equipment is required for viewing.
Source: Described and Captioned Media Program
National Association of the Deaf
4211 Church Street Ext.
Roebuck, SC 29376
Phone: 1-800-237-6213
Fax: 1-800-538-5636
World Wide Web URL: http://www.dcmp.org

General Chemistry Online!

Provides tutorials, quizzes and exams, diagrams, and an "Ask Antoine" section designed to help students learn general chemistry.

Availability: All requesters
Suggested Grade: 9-Adult
Order Number: not applicable
Format: Web Site
Source: Fred Senese
World Wide Web URL:
http://antoine.frostburg.edu/chem/senese/101

Hi! Hydrogen

Facts about hydrogen, lab safety rules, warning labels, and an introduction to chromatography and filtration.

Availability: All requesters
Suggested Grade: 9-12
Order Number: not applicable
Format: Web Site
Special Notes: This URL will lead you to a subject page. Then click on the appropriate subject heading.

Source: ThinkQuest
World Wide Web URL:
http://www.thinkquest.org/pls/html/think.library

Hyper Chemistry, On the Web

Almost anything any student or teacher might wish to learn about chemistry.

Availability: All requesters
Suggested Grade: 9-Adult
Order Number: not applicable
Format: Web Site
Special Notes: This URL will lead you to a subject page. Then click on the appropriate subject heading.
Source: ThinkQuest
World Wide Web URL:
http://www.thinkquest.org/pls/html/think.library

Lab Safety WebQuest

Students will be engaged in gathering information on laboratory safety, how to use safety equipment, and how to avoid accidents.

Availability: All requesters
Suggested Grade: 9-12
Order Number: not applicable
Format: WebQuest
Source: Donna Marie Blakeney
World Wide Web URL:
http://dvhs.dvusd.org/Science/LabSafety/index.html

Periodic Library

An interactive period table of the elements.

Availability: All requesters
Suggested Grade: 9-12
Platform: Windows
Order Number: not applicable
Format: Downloadable FULL PROGRAM
Source: Boolean Dream Inc.
World Wide Web URL: http://www.orbit.org/perlib/

Periodic Table Adventure

Includes lessons on the history of the periodic table, a WebQuest, and more lessons to make learning about the periodic table fun.

Availability: All requesters
Suggested Grade: 6-12
Order Number: not applicable
Format: Web Site
Source: D. Gibson
World Wide Web URL:
http://web.buddyproject.org/web017/web017/

Pre-University Chemistry Course

Lots of teaching material based on the book "Chemistry, Matter and the Universe."

Availability: All requesters
Suggested Grade: 9-12
Order Number: not applicable
Format: Online Curriculum

Source: Richard E. Dickerson and Irving Geis
World Wide Web URL:
http://neon.chem.ox.ac.uk/vrchemistry/foundation.html

Processing of Castor Meal for Detoxification & Deallergenation, The
Describes this process.
Availability: Single copies to schools, libraries, and homeschoolers in the United States and Canada. Make request on official stationery.
Suggested Grade: 9-Adult
Order Number: order by title
Format: Bulletin
Source: International Castor Oil Association, The
24 Burton Avenue
Woodmere, NY 11598
Fax: 1-516-569-6940
Email Address: icoa@icoa.org

Reactions in Chemistry
An eight-part workshop for the professional development of high school chemistry and physical science teachers
Availability: All requesters
Suggested Grade: 9-Adult
Order Number: not applicable
Production Date: 2003
Format: Streaming Video
Terms: A simple FREE registration is required to view videos.
Source: Annenberg Media
World Wide Web URL:
http://www.learner.org/resources/browse.html

Science is Fun
This chemistry professional shares the fun of science through home science activities, demonstration shows, and more.
Availability: All requesters
Suggested Grade: All ages
Order Number: not applicable
Format: Web Site
Source: Bassam Z. Shakhashiri
World Wide Web URL: http://scifun.chem.wisc.edu/

Web Elements
All sorts of information related to the periodic table of the elements is found here.
Availability: All requesters
Suggested Grade: 9-Adult
Order Number: not applicable
Format: Web Site
Source: Dr. Mark Winter
World Wide Web URL:
http://www.webelements.com/http://www.webelements.com/

Indicates an Internet Resource--just enter the URL and instantly access the FREE teaching aid you need!
All materials listed in this 2010-2011 edition are BRAND NEW!

3

CONSERVATION EDUCATION

Acid Deposition

Defines acid deposition and discusses risk factors, ecological effects and impacts, and what scientists are doing to better understand the problem.

Availability: All requesters
Suggested Grade: 6-Adult
Order Number: not applicable
Format: Online Fact Sheet

Source: Ecological Society of America, The
World Wide Web URL:
http://www.esa.org/education_diversity/factsheets.php

Acid Rain Revisited

Addresses what has happened since the 1990 Clean Air Act Amendments.

Availability: All requesters
Suggested Grade: 6-Adult
Order Number: not applicable
Format: Online Fact Sheet

Source: Ecological Society of America, The
World Wide Web URL:
http://www.esa.org/education_diversity/factsheets.php

Acid Rain WebQuest

Explores the definition of acid rain and discusses its effects.

Availability: All requesters
Suggested Grade: 5-8
Order Number: not applicable
Format: WebQuest

Source: Gerald Robillard
World Wide Web URL:
http://www.netfiles.org/lessons/acidrain.shtml

Adventures of the Camouflage Kid

Camouflage Kid is on litter patrol in his community. He finds evidence that three students are throwing their garbage on the ground and polluting their environment. He explains that litter not only pollutes our clean beaches, but can end up in the ocean and threaten animal life.

Availability: Schools, libraries, and homeschoolers in Connecticut, Maine, Massachusetts, New Hampshire, Rhode Island, and Vermont.
Suggested Grade: 4-Adult
Order Number: VID 161
Format: VHS videotape
Terms: Borrower pays return postage. Return within three weeks of receipt. If the tape you request is available, it will be mailed within 5 business days. If not, you will be notified that this video is already out on loan. No more than three titles may be borrowed by one requestor at a time. No reservations for a specific date will be accepted. It is most efficient to order via the web site.

Source: U. S. Environmental Protection Agency, Region 1
Customer Service Center
One Congress Street, Suite 1100
Boston, MA 02214
World Wide Web URL:
http://yosemite.epa.gov/r1/videolen.nsf/

Air Quality--Ozone

Discusses the importance of ozone and the harm of the deterioration that it is facing.

Availability: Schools, libraries, and homeschoolers in Connecticut, Maine, Massachusetts, New Hampshire, Rhode Island, and Vermont.
Suggested Grade: 9-12
Order Number: C-98-12
Production Date: 1998
Format: VHS videotape
Terms: Borrower pays return postage. Return within three weeks of receipt. If the tape you request is available, it will be mailed within 5 business days. If not, you will be notified that this video is already out on loan. No more than three titles may be borrowed by one requestor at a time. No reservations for a specific date will be accepted. It is most efficient to order via the web site.

Source: U. S. Environmental Protection Agency, Region 1
Customer Service Center
One Congress Street, Suite 1100
Boston, MA 02214
http://yosemite.epa.gov/r1/videolen.nsf/

Air You Breathe, The

Interviews with professionals and patients provide information on polluted air inside and outside, how it is caused, and what can be done about it. Relates effects of breathing in polluted air such as asthma and other diseases.

Availability: Schools, libraries, and homeschoolers in the United States who serve the hearing impaired.
Suggested Grade: 9-Adult
Order Number: 13289
Production Date: 2000
Format: DVD
Special Notes: Also available as live streaming video over the Internet.
Terms: Sponsor pays all transportation costs. Return one week after receipt. Participation is limited to deaf or hard of hearing Americans, their parents, families, teachers, counselors, or others whose use would benefit a deaf or hard of hearing person. Only one person in the audience needs to be hearing impaired. You must register--which is free. These videos are all open-captioned--no special equipment is required for viewing.

Source: Described and Captioned Media Program
National Association of the Deaf
4211 Church Street Ext.
Roebuck, SC 29376
Phone: 1-800-237-6213
Fax: 1-800-538-5636
World Wide Web URL: http://www.dcmp.org

Alternative Is Conservation

A documentary on water conservation with good examples of communities changing to water conservation techniques.

Availability: Schools, libraries, and homeschoolers in Connecticut, Maine, Massachusetts, New Hampshire, Rhode Island, and Vermont.
Suggested Grade: 7-12

 Indicates an Internet Resource--just enter the URL and instantly access the FREE teaching aid you need!
All materials listed in this 2010-2011 edition are BRAND NEW!

Order Number: VID 096
Production Date: 1980
Format: VHS videotape
Terms: Borrower pays return postage. Return within three weeks of receipt. If the tape you request is available, it will be mailed within 5 business days. If not, you will be notified that this video is already out on loan. No more than three titles may be borrowed by one requestor at a time. No reservations for a specific date will be accepted. It is most efficient to order via the web site.

Source: U. S. Environmental Protection Agency, Region 1
Customer Service Center
One Congress Street, Suite 1100
Boston, MA 02214
World Wide Web URL:
http://yosemite.epa.gov/r1/videolen.nsf/

Alu-Man The Can

Teaches young students about recycling--Alu-Man, an animated aluminum can, searches for a recycling center.

Availability: Schools, libraries, and homeschoolers in Connecticut, Maine, Massachusetts, New Hampshire, Rhode Island, and Vermont.
Suggested Grade: K-3
Order Number: VID RL2
Format: VHS videotape
Terms: Borrower pays return postage. Return within three weeks of receipt. If the tape you request is available, it will be mailed within 5 business days. If not, you will be notified that this video is already out on loan. No more than three titles may be borrowed by one requestor at a time. No reservations for a specific date will be accepted. It is most efficient to order via the web site.

Source: U. S. Environmental Protection Agency, Region 1
Customer Service Center
One Congress Street, Suite 1100
Boston, MA 02214
World Wide Web URL:
http://yosemite.epa.gov/r1/videolen.nsf/

Amazonia - Minimum Critical Size of Ecosystems

Explores ecological complexity of the rainforest and the minimum area of undisturbed forest necessary to support each member of various species.

Availability: Schools, libraries, and nursing homes in the United States.
Suggested Grade: 6-12
Order Number: GEBRA7-video
Production Date: 1987
Format: VHS videotape
Terms: Borrowers must have a User's Agreement on file with this source--available by mail or via the Internet. Return postage is paid by borrower; return 12 days after showing. Book at least three weeks in advance. All borrowers are limited to a total of ten items per semester.

Source: Latin American Resource Center
Stone Center for Latin American Studies
Tulane University, 100 Jones Hall
New Orleans, LA 70118

Phone: 1-504-862-3143
Fax: 1-504-865-6719
World Wide Web URL:
http://stonecenter.tulane.edu/LARCLLCatalogue.htm
Email Address: crcrts@tulane.edu

America's Endangered Species: Don't Say Goodbye

Can a picture save a species? Photographers Susan Middleton and David Litittschwager are in a race against the clock to capture powerful portraits of America's most threatened creatures. Join them on this unforgettable adventure as every picture tells story and makes a plea: DON'T SAY GOODBYE to America's natural treasures.

Availability: Schools, libraries, homeschoolers, and nursing homes in Illinois, Indiana, Iowa, Michigan, Minnesota, Missouri, Ohio, and Wisconsin only.
Suggested Grade: 3-12
Order Number: 11
Production Date: 1997
Format: VHS videotape
Terms: Return postage is paid by borrower. Book 10-14 days in advance. Return 7 days after showing. Please provide alternate showing date.

Source: U. S. Fish and Wildlife Service
Region 3, Resource Library
3815 American Boulevard
Bloomington, MN 55425
Fax: 1-612-725-3279
Email Address: judy_geck@fws.gov

Ancient Sea Turtles: The Last Voyage?

The video provides an overview of the extraordinary natural history of sea turtles and vividly exposes the major threats to these giant reptiles. Biologists and environmentalists describe the international efforts to save one of the oldest living links with the past.

Availability: Schools, libraries, homeschoolers, and nursing homes in Illinois, Indiana, Iowa, Michigan, Minnesota, Missouri, Ohio, and Wisconsin only.
Suggested Grade: 6-12
Order Number: 342
Format: VHS videotape
Terms: Return postage is paid by borrower. Book 10-14 days in advance. Return 7 days after showing. Please provide alternate showing date.

Source: U. S. Fish and Wildlife Service
Region 3, Resource Library
3815 American Boulevard
Bloomington, MN 55425
Fax: 1-612-725-3279
Email Address: judy_geck@fws.gov

Backyard Conservation and Local Laws

Introduces students to the process of making laws that while reflecting community values may help or hinder backyard conservation efforts.

Indicates an Internet Resource--just enter the URL and instantly access the FREE teaching aid you need!
*All materials listed in this 2010-2011 edition are **BRAND NEW**!*

Availability: All requesters
Suggested Grade: 6-12
Order Number: not applicable
Format: Online Lesson Plan
Source: Wildlife Habitat Council
World Wide Web URL:
http://www.wildlifehc.org/managementtools/
backyard-lessonplans.cfm

Balancing Act

Environmental enhancement is a major effort of the State Water Contractors. Learn what types of projects are being developed to offset environmental impacts of State Water Project construction and operation.

Availability: Schools, libraries, homeschoolers, and nursing homes in the United States.
Suggested Grade: 6-Adult
Order Number: order by title
Format: DVD
Special Notes: A number of titles from this organization are included on this DVD.
Terms: Borrower pays return postage. Return within 14 days after scheduled use, via UPS or Federal Express. Book at least 14 days in advance and include alternate date. Requests should include title(s), format, name of responsible person, organizational affiliation, phone, and complete delivery address. No part of any program can be used or duplicated without prior written permission. All programs are available for purchase at a nominal fee. May be available in other formats; inquire if interested. Online video previews are available.
Source: California Department of Water Resources
Attn: Video Library, Room 204-22
P. O. Box 942836
Sacramento, CA 94236-0001
Phone: 1-916-653-4893
Fax: 1-916-653-3310
World Wide Web URL: http://www.water.ca.gov/
Email Address: www.publicawillm@water.ca.gov

Balancing Act

Environmental enhancement is a major effort of the State Water Contractors. Learn what types of projects are being developed to offset environmental impacts of State Water Project construction and operation.

Availability: Schools, libraries, homeschoolers, and nursing homes in the United States.
Suggested Grade: 6-Adult
Order Number: order by title
Format: VHS videotape
Special Notes: Closed captioned.
Terms: Borrower pays return postage. Return within 14 days after scheduled use, via UPS or Federal Express. Book at least 14 days in advance and include alternate date. Requests should include title(s), format, name of responsible person, organizational affiliation, phone, and complete delivery address. No part of any program can be used or duplicated without prior written permission. All programs are available for purchase at a nominal fee. May be available in other formats; inquire if interested. Online video previews are available.
Source: California Department of Water Resources
Attn: Video Library, Room 204-22
P. O. Box 942836
Sacramento, CA 94236-0001
Phone: 1-916-653-4893
Fax: 1-916-653-3310
World Wide Web URL: http://www.water.ca.gov/
Email Address: www.publicawillm@water.ca.gov

Balancing Nature--Trapping In Today's World (Short Version)

Senator Beck investigates a veterinarian office, the state's fish and wildlife agency, a sheep ranch and a beaver dam on a sleepy residential creek where she discovers emotions about trapping can run high. The purpose of this search is to gather information to fulfill her quest for a fair resolution of trapping issues and preservation of the delicate balance between nature and civilization.

Availability: Schools, libraries, homeschoolers, and nursing homes in Illinois, Indiana, Iowa, Michigan, Minnesota, Missouri, Ohio, and Wisconsin only.
Suggested Grade: 9-12
Order Number: 230
Production Date: 1996
Format: VHS videotape
Terms: Return postage is paid by borrower. Book 10-14 days in advance. Return 7 days after showing. Please provide alternate showing date.
Source: U. S. Fish and Wildlife Service
Region 3, Resource Library
3815 American Boulevard
Bloomington, MN 55425
Fax: 1-612-725-3279
Email Address: judy_geck@fws.gov

Balancing Wildlife and Agriculture-U.S. Prairie Pothole Joint Venture

Conservation groups, individual states, and government join in the "Joint Venture" to protect waterfowl habitat. Still shots are used.

Availability: Schools, libraries, homeschoolers, and nursing homes in Illinois, Indiana, Iowa, Michigan, Minnesota, Missouri, Ohio, and Wisconsin only.
Suggested Grade: 9-12
Order Number: 28
Format: VHS videotape
Terms: Return postage is paid by borrower. Book 10-14 days in advance. Return 7 days after showing. Please provide alternate showing date.
Source: U. S. Fish and Wildlife Service
Region 3, Resource Library
3815 American Boulevard
Bloomington, MN 55425

Fax: 1-612-725-3279
Email Address: judy_geck@fws.gov

Basics of Geology Series

Discusses erosion and weathering, mountains, volcanoes, earthquakes, and much more.

Availability: All requesters through interlibrary loan.
Suggested Grade: 5-12
Order Number: 204 B3742 1998 VIDEOC
Production Date: 1998
Format: Set of 4 VHS videotapes
Special Notes: Includes a teacher's guide.
Terms: These videotapes are available through interlibrary loan only. Simply request the specific video by name and number at your local public library, university library, or company library. The librarian will submit your request using an ALA interlibrary loan form, and the videos will be mailed to your library for your use. Interlibrary loans are limited to two videos at a time. The address listed below is for the ALA loan form only--your librarian must submit requests to this address.

Source: U. S. Geological Survey Library
345 Middlefield Road, MS 955
Menlo Park, CA 94025

Being Water-Wise Outdoors

Find the answers to your outdoor watering questions.

Availability: All requesters
Suggested Grade: 6-Adult
Languages: English; Spanish
Order Number: not applicable
Format: Downloadable Brochure

Source: Texas Water Development Board
World Wide Web URL:
http://www.twdb.state.tx.us/assistance/conservation/pubs.asp

Black Water

Study of effects of water pollution on the maritime community of Bahai in Brazil.

Availability: Schools, libraries, and nursing homes in the United States.
Suggested Grade: 6-12
Order Number: GEBRA10-video
Production Date: 1990
Format: VHS videotape
Terms: Borrowers must have a User's Agreement on file with this source--available by mail or via the Internet. Return postage is paid by borrower; return 12 days after showing. Book at least three weeks in advance. All borrowers are limited to a total of ten items per semester.

Source: Latin American Resource Center
Stone Center for Latin American Studies
Tulane University, 100 Jones Hall
New Orleans, LA 70118
Phone: 1-504-862-3143
Fax: 1-504-865-6719
World Wide Web URL:
http://stonecenter.tulane.edu/LARCLLCatalogue.htm
Email Address: crcrts@tulane.edu

Borrowed from Our Future

With increasing poverty and a changing environment, the world's future may be in jeopardy. Some community-based alternatives to increase local food supply, and provide jobs without exhausting resources, are offered. The video warns that with the fragile state of environment, people everywhere must work together to find solutions before it is too late to redeem our future.

Availability: Schools, libraries, homeschoolers, and nursing homes in the United States.
Suggested Grade: 9-Adult
Order Number: order by title
Format: VHS videotape
Terms: Borrower pays return postage. Return the day after scheduled showing, via UPS or Priority Mail, insured for $100.00. Book 4 weeks in advance and include an alternate date. Order should include name of person responsible for handling the video, and complete mailing address. Please mention this Guide when ordering. Tapes may not be duplicated, edited or exhibited for a fee.

Source: Church World Service
Film & Video Library
28606 Phillips Street, P. O. Box 968
Elkhart, IN 46515
Phone: 1-800-297-1516, ext. 338
Fax: 1-574-262-0966
World Wide Web URL: http://www.churchworldservice.org
Email Address: videos@churchworldservice.org

Breaking Ground

This program examines the problem in Nepal, Kenya, and the U.S. finds not only devastation but also some current solutions: forestation, protective planning, and new cutting techniques.

Availability: Schools, libraries, homeschoolers, and nursing homes in Illinois, Indiana, Iowa, Michigan, Minnesota, Missouri, Ohio, and Wisconsin only.
Suggested Grade: 9-12
Order Number: 322
Format: VHS videotape
Terms: Return postage is paid by borrower. Book 10-14 days in advance. Return 7 days after showing. Please provide alternate showing date.

Source: U. S. Fish and Wildlife Service
Region 3, Resource Library
3815 American Boulevard
Bloomington, MN 55425
Fax: 1-612-725-3279
Email Address: judy_geck@fws.gov

Bright Sparks: Energy

Cartoon characters explore conventional and contemporary energy sources. Visit an oil rig, a coal mine, and hydroelectric power plant. Experience nuclear fusion and fission, wind, solar, wave and tidal power. Visit a Spanish convection-operated "tower of power." Observe energy-

 Indicates an Internet Resource--just enter the URL and instantly access the FREE teaching aid you need!
All materials listed in this 2010-2011 edition are BRAND NEW!

7

efficient vehicles and buildings so constructed that over 90 energy-saving functions occur. This study also contemplates energy conservation and the controversial "greenhouse" effect.

Availability: Schools, libraries, homeschoolers, and nursing homes in the United States.
Suggested Grade: 1-8
Order Number: order by title
Format: VHS videotape
Terms: Borrower pays return postage. Return the day after scheduled showing, via UPS or Priority Mail, insured for $100.00. Book 4 weeks in advance and include an alternate date. Order should include name of person responsible for handling the video, and complete mailing address. Please mention this Guide when ordering. Tapes may not be duplicated, edited or exhibited for a fee.
Source: Church World Service
Film & Video Library
28606 Phillips Street, P. O. Box 968
Elkhart, IN 46515
Phone: 1-800-297-1516, ext. 338
Fax: 1-574-262-0966
World Wide Web URL: http://www.churchworldservice.org
Email Address: videos@churchworldservice.org

California's Changing Forest: A Case for Management
Examines both sides of the controversy over forest use and forest sustainability. Explores the impact of mankind on his environment and the dependence he has formed on natural resources.

Availability: Schools, libraries, and homeschoolers in the United States and Canada.
Suggested Grade: 7-12
Order Number: order by title
Format: VHS videotape
Terms: Borrower pays return postage. Return within 15 to 30 days after receipt via United States mail. Provide alternate showing date.
Source: The Forest Foundation
853 Lincoln Way, Suite 104
Auburn, CA 95603
Phone: 1-866-241-8733
Fax: 1-530-823-1850
World Wide Web URL: http://www.calforestfoundation.org

Can Polar Bears Tread Water?
Calls attention to the graphic examples illustrating the changes in the earth's atmosphere due to excessive emissions of chlorofluorocarbons, carbon dioxide, and methane gasses.

Availability: Schools, libraries, homeschoolers, and nursing homes in Illinois, Indiana, Iowa, Michigan, Minnesota, Missouri, Ohio, and Wisconsin only.
Suggested Grade: 9-12
Order Number: 320
Format: VHS videotape

Terms: Return postage is paid by borrower. Book 10-14 days in advance. Return 7 days after showing. Please provide alternate showing date.
Source: U. S. Fish and Wildlife Service
Region 3, Resource Library
3815 American Boulevard
Bloomington, MN 55425
Fax: 1-612-725-3279
Email Address: judy_geck@fws.gov

Can Tropical Rainforests Be Saved?
Discussion on the use of trees as currency, sovereign rights of nations and indigenous people, and medical and economic use for forest flora.

Availability: Schools in the United States.
Suggested Grade: 6-12
Order Number: order by title
Production Date: 1991
Format: VHS videotape
Terms: Borrower pays return postage. Return 14 days after receipt, via USPS including insurance. All borrowers must have a current lending agreement on file with the Outreach program. This agreement is available via the web site or may be requested via phone or fax.
Source: Center for Latin American Studies
University of Florida
319 Grinter Hall
P. O. Box 115530
Gainesville, FL 32611-5530
Phone: 1-352-392-0375
Fax: 1-352-392-7682
World Wide Web URL: http://www.latam.ufl.edu/outreach
Email Address: maryr@ufl.edu

Can Tropical Rainforests Be Saved?
Discussion on the use of trees as currency, sovereign rights of nations and indigenous people, and medical and economic use for forest flora.

Availability: Schools, libraries, and nursing homes in the United States.
Suggested Grade: 6-12
Order Number: GE14-video
Production Date: 1992
Format: VHS videotape
Terms: Borrowers must have a User's Agreement on file with this source--available by mail or via the Internet. Return postage is paid by borrower; return 12 days after showing. Book at least three weeks in advance. All borrowers are limited to a total of ten items per semester.
Source: Latin American Resource Center
Stone Center for Latin American Studies
Tulane University
100 Jones Hall
New Orleans, LA 70118
Phone: 1-504-862-3143
Fax: 1-504-865-6719
World Wide Web URL:
http://stonecenter.tulane.edu/LARCLLCatalogue.htm
Email Address: crcrts@tulane.edu

Case of the Mysterious Macros, The
Teaches students how to investigate the health of a local stream by using macroinvertebrates to learn about water quality.

Availability:	All requesters
Suggested Grade:	4-8
Order Number:	not applicable
Format:	Web Site
Special Notes:	This URL will lead you to a subject page. Then click on the appropriate subject heading.

Source: ThinkQuest
World Wide Web URL:
http://www.thinkquest.org/pls/html/think.library

Challenge of Global Warming, The
Scientifically looks at ways to dispose of air polluting carbon.

Availability:	Schools, libraries, homeschoolers, and nursing homes in Connecticut (except Fairfield County), Maine, Massachusetts, New Hampshire, Rhode Island, and Vermont.
Suggested Grade:	6-12
Order Number:	557
Format:	VHS videotape
Terms:	Borrower pays return postage, including insurance. Return two weeks after receipt.

Source: Consulate General of Japan, Boston
Federal Reserve Plaza, 14th Floor
600 Atlantic Avenue
Boston, MA 02210
Phone: 1-617-973-9772
Fax: 1-617-542-1329
World Wide Web URL:
http://www.boston.us.emb-japan.go.jp
Email Address: infocul@cgjbos.org

Challenge of Global Warming, The
Scientifically looks at ways to dispose of air polluting carbon.

Availability:	Schools, libraries, and nursing homes in Hawaii.
Suggested Grade:	6-12
Order Number:	NA-29
Format:	VHS videotape
Terms:	Borrower pays return postage. A maximum of 3 videos may be borrowed per person. Return within one week of date borrowed.

Source: Consulate General of Japan, Honolulu
1742 Nuuanu Avenue
Honolulu, HI 96817-3294
Phone: 1-808-543-3111
Fax: 1-808-543-3170
World Wide Web URL:
http://www.honolulu.us.emb-japan.go.jp

Charlie Chestnut Curriculum Manual
A complete curriculum manual for helping students learn more about this disappearing tree.

Availability:	All requesters
Suggested Grade:	4-8
Order Number:	not applicable
Format:	Downloadable Curriculum

Source: American Chestnut Foundation, The
World Wide Web URL:
http://www.charliechestnut.org/Phase1/Teachers/
Teachers.html

Chesapeake Bay Link
Includes lesson plans and activities that examine the interaction of humans and the bay.

Availability:	All requesters
Suggested Grade:	6-12
Order Number:	not applicable
Format:	Web Site

Source: Baylink.org
World Wide Web URL: http://www.baylink.org/

Circle of Life
Reviews the link between mankind and the environment. It explores in depth the precept that every act of consumption has a natural consequence somewhere. Reviews the topics of renewable resources, responsible consumerism and disposal, and the stewardship of the land.

Availability:	Schools, libraries, and homeschoolers in the United States and Canada.
Suggested Grade:	5-12
Order Number:	order by title
Format:	VHS videotape
Terms:	Borrower pays return postage. Return within 15 to 30 days after receipt via United States mail. Provide alternate showing date.

Source: The Forest Foundation
853 Lincoln Way, Suite 104
Auburn, CA 95603
Phone: 1-866-241-8733
Fax: 1-530-823-1850
World Wide Web URL: http://www.calforestfoundation.org

Close the Loop: Buy Recycled
A program to educate businesses, institutions, government, and consumers on how (and why) to purchase goods with recycled content.

Availability:	Schools, libraries, and homeschoolers in Connecticut, Maine, Massachusetts, New Hampshire, Rhode Island, and Vermont.
Suggested Grade:	7-12
Order Number:	RL9
Production Date:	1995
Format:	VHS videotape
Terms:	Borrower pays return postage. Return within three weeks of receipt. If the tape you request is available, it will be mailed within 5 business days. If not, you will be notified that this video is already out on loan. No more than three titles may be borrowed by one requestor at a time. No reservations for a specific date will be accepted. It is most efficient to order via the web site.

 Indicates an Internet Resource--just enter the URL and instantly access the FREE teaching aid you need!
All materials listed in this 2010-2011 edition are BRAND NEW!

9

CONSERVATION EDUCATION

Source: U. S. Environmental Protection Agency, Region 1
Customer Service Center
One Congress Street, Suite 1100
Boston, MA 02214
World Wide Web URL:
http://yosemite.epa.gov/r1/videolen.nsf/

Colorado River Facts
This booklet was developed to educate about the importance of water in an arid region and how it relates to this vast river.

Availability: Limit of 10 copies to schools, libraries, and homeschoolers world-wide.
Suggested Grade: 6-12
Languages: English; Spanish
Order Number: order by title
Format: Booklet

Source: Water Education Foundation
Education Director
717 K Street, Suite 317
Sacramento, CA 95814
Phone: 1-916-444-6240
Fax: 1-916-448-7699
World Wide Web URL: http://www.watereducation.org
Email Address: dfarmer@watereducation.org

Conservation
Using Missouri's Department of Conservation as an example, Ms. Jennings and her students learn about different aspects of conservation. Briefly reviews its history before exploring its importance in saving forests, wildlife, rivers, and soil. Emphasizes the interdependence of all life forms and what people can do to conserve natural resources. Focuses on Missouri's endangered species.

Availability: Schools, libraries, and homeschoolers in the United States who serve the hearing impaired.
Suggested Grade: 4-8
Order Number: 13116
Production Date: 1998
Format: DVD
Special Notes: Produced by Oakleaf Productions.
Terms: Sponsor pays all transportation costs. Return one week after receipt. Participation is limited to deaf or hard of hearing Americans, their parents, families, teachers, counselors, or others whose use would benefit a deaf or hard of hearing person. Only one person in the audience needs to be hearing impaired. You must register--which is free. These videos are all open-captioned--no special equipment is required for viewing.

Source: Described and Captioned Media Program
National Association of the Deaf
4211 Church Street Ext.
Roebuck, SC 29376
Phone: 1-800-237-6213
Fax: 1-800-538-5636
World Wide Web URL: http://www.dcmp.org

Dream Park Lesson Plan
Students will be able to explain the factors in planting a tree as well as exploring landscape architecture.

Availability: All requesters
Suggested Grade: 5-8
Order Number: not applicable
Format: Online Lesson Plan

Source: Janet Bartlett
World Wide Web URL:
http://sftrc.cas.psu.edu/LessonPlans/Forestry/
DreamPark.html

Earth Buddies
Designed to provide information to help people improve the environment.

Availability: All requesters
Suggested Grade: 4-12
Order Number: not applicable
Format: Web Site
Special Notes: This URL will lead you to a subject page. Then click on the appropriate subject heading.

Source: ThinkQuest
World Wide Web URL:
http://www.thinkquest.org/pls/html/think.library

EarthTrends
A free online database that focuses on issues of sustainable development and the environment.

Availability: All requesters
Suggested Grade: 9-Adult
Order Number: not applicable
Format: Online Database

Source: World Resources Institute
World Wide Web URL: http://earthtrends.wri.org/

Ecosystem Services
Defines ecosystems, the services or resources they produce, and the threats to these resources.

Availability: All requesters
Suggested Grade: 6-Adult
Order Number: not applicable
Format: Online Fact Sheet

Source: Ecological Society of America, The
World Wide Web URL:
http://www.esa.org/education_diversity/factsheets.php

Elementary School Lesson Plans
Activities to introduce students to water systems, water management, and water conservation.

Availability: All requesters
Suggested Grade: 2-6
Order Number: not applicable
Format: Online Lesson Plans

Source: Portland Water Bureau
World Wide Web URL:
http://www.portlandonline.com/water/index.cfm?c=daadc

Emissions and Emotions: Challenges to the European Forest
Focuses on the ecological crisis in an area of Eastern Europe known as the Death Triangle.
Availability: Schools, libraries, homeschoolers, and nursing homes in the United States.
Suggested Grade: 9-12
Order Number: order by title
Production Date: 1992
Format: VHS videotape
Terms: Borrower pays return postage. Return the day after scheduled showing, via UPS or Priority Mail, insured for $100.00. Book 4 weeks in advance and include an alternate date. Order should include name of person responsible for handling the video, and complete mailing address. Please mention this Guide when ordering. Tapes may not be duplicated, edited or exhibited for a fee.
Source: Church World Service
Film & Video Library
28606 Phillips Street, P. O. Box 968
Elkhart, IN 46515
Phone: 1-800-297-1516, ext. 338
Fax: 1-574-262-0966
World Wide Web URL: http://www.churchworldservice.org
Email Address: videos@churchworldservice.org

Endangered Species Instructional Slide Program: Endangered Means There's Still Time
Set of endangered species slides designed to provide a visual instruction component to learning about endangered species. Students will: benefit from seeing endangered species in their natural surroundings, learn about the causes of their problems, and efforts to protect species in danger. Program is suitable for students in grades four through twelve.
Availability: Schools, libraries, homeschoolers, and nursing homes in Illinois, Indiana, Iowa, Michigan, Minnesota, Missouri, Ohio, and Wisconsin only.
Suggested Grade: 4-12
Order Number: 15
Production Date: 1996
Format: Set of 59 slides
Special Notes: Includes a script and quiz.
Terms: Return postage is paid by borrower. Book 10-14 days in advance. Return 7 days after showing. Please provide alternate showing date.
Source: U. S. Fish and Wildlife Service
Region 3, Resource Library
3815 American Boulevard
Bloomington, MN 55425
Fax: 1-612-725-3279
Email Address: judy_geck@fws.gov

Endangered Species Act-An American Legacy
Explains this law written to protect wildlife.

Availability: Schools, libraries, homeschoolers, and nursing homes in Illinois, Indiana, Iowa, Michigan, Minnesota, Missouri, Ohio, and Wisconsin only.
Suggested Grade: 7-12
Order Number: 439
Format: VHS videotape
Terms: Return postage is paid by borrower. Book 10-14 days in advance. Return 7 days after showing. Please provide alternate showing date.
Source: U. S. Fish and Wildlife Service
Region 3, Resource Library
3815 American Boulevard
Bloomington, MN 55425
Fax: 1-612-725-3279
Email Address: judy_geck@fws.gov

Endangered/Threatened Species
A listing of the mollusks, fish, amphibians, reptiles, birds, mammals, and crustaceans declared by this agency to be endangered or threatened.
Availability: All requesters
Suggested Grade: All ages
Order Number: not applicable
Format: Online Article
Special Notes: This is a PDF file which will open automatically on your computer.
Source: Tennessee Wildlife Resources Agency
World Wide Web URL:
http://tennessee.gov/twra/pdfs/endangered.pdf

Environmental Justice
Defines environmental justice and addresses the causes, effects, history, and role of ecology in environmental justice.
Availability: All requesters
Suggested Grade: 6-Adult
Order Number: not applicable
Format: Online Fact Sheet
Source: Ecological Society of America, The
World Wide Web URL:
http://www.esa.org/education_diversity/factsheets.php

Environmental Literacy
Discusses this issue.
Availability: All requesters
Suggested Grade: Teacher Reference
Order Number: not applicable
Production Date: 1992
Format: Online Article
Source: John F. Disinger and Charles E. Roth
World Wide Web URL: http://www.ericdigests.org/
1992-1/literacy.htm

Environment Latest Approaches
Covers various aspects of preserving nature and the environment.

CONSERVATION EDUCATION

Availability: Schools, libraries, homeschoolers, and nursing homes in Connecticut (except Fairfield County), Maine, Massachusetts, New Hampshire, Rhode Island, and Vermont.
Suggested Grade: 6-12
Order Number: 560
Format: VHS videotape
Terms: Borrower pays return postage, including insurance. Return two weeks after receipt.

**Source: Consulate General of Japan, Boston
Federal Reserve Plaza, 14th Floor
600 Atlantic Avenue
Boston, MA 02210
Phone: 1-617-973-9772
Fax: 1-617-542-1329
World Wide Web URL:
http://www.boston.us.emb-japan.go.jp
Email Address: infocul@cgjbos.org**

Environment Latest Approaches

Covers various aspects of preserving nature and the environment.
Availability: Schools, libraries, and nursing homes in Hawaii.
Suggested Grade: 6-12
Order Number: NA-27
Format: VHS videotape
Terms: Borrower pays return postage. A maximum of 3 videos may be borrowed per person. Return within one week of date borrowed.

**Source: Consulate General of Japan, Honolulu
1742 Nuuanu Avenue
Honolulu, HI 96817-3294
Phone: 1-808-543-3111
Fax: 1-808-543-3170
World Wide Web URL:
http://www.honolulu.us.emb-japan.go.jp**

Environment Under Fire: Ecology and Politics in Central America

Central America's endangered natural environment means increased poverty among its people. Rainforest destruction, deadly pesticide use, the effects of cash cropping, and continuing conflict plague the region. Top Central American and U. S. environmentalists explore the issues and potential solution.
Availability: Schools and libraries in Iowa, Illinois, Michigan, Minnesota, and Wisconsin.
Suggested Grade: 9-Adult
Order Number: ENVCAEN8VHS
Production Date: 1988
Format: VHS videotape
Terms: Borrower pays return postage. Return 8 days after showing. Book 2 weeks in advance. Order may also be picked up for those near the Center.

**Source: Center for Latin American and Caribbean Studies
UW-Milwaukee
P. O. Box 413
Milwaukee, WI 53201**

**Phone: 1-414-229-5987
World Wide Web URL: http://www.uwm.edu/Dept/CLACS
Email Address: audvis@usm.edu**

Environment Under Fire: Ecology and Politics in Central America

Central America's endangered natural environment means increased poverty among its people. Rainforest destruction, deadly pesticide use, the effects of cash cropping, and continuing conflict plague the region. Top Central American and U. S. environmentalists explore the issues and potential solution.
Availability: Schools, libraries, homeschoolers, and nursing homes in the United States.
Suggested Grade: 9-Adult
Order Number: order by title
Production Date: 1988
Format: VHS videotape
Terms: Borrower pays return postage. Return the day after scheduled showing, via UPS or Priority Mail, insured for $100.00. Book 4 weeks in advance and include an alternate date. Order should include name of person responsible for handling the video, and complete mailing address. Please mention this Guide when ordering. Tapes may not be duplicated, edited or exhibited for a fee.

**Source: Church World Service
Film & Video Library
28606 Phillips Street, P. O. Box 968
Elkhart, IN 46515
Phone: 1-800-297-1516, ext. 338
Fax: 1-574-262-0966
World Wide Web URL: http://www.churchworldservice.org
Email Address: videos@churchworldservice.org**

Extreme Ice

An acclaimed photographer teams up with scientists to document the runaway melting of arctic glaciers.
Availability: All requesters
Suggested Grade: 7-Adult
Order Number: not applicable
Production Date: 2009
Format: Streaming Video

**Source: NOVA
World Wide Web URL:
http://www.pbs.org/wgbh/nova/programs/index.html**

Eye on Conservation Lesson Plans

Lessons for teaching students about ecological concepts and endangered species in Georgia.
Availability: All requesters
Suggested Grade: All ages
Order Number: not applicable
Format: Online Lesson Plans

**Source: Georgia Museum of Natural History
World Wide Web URL:
http://museum.nhm.uga.edu/content/exhibits/conservation/
lesson_plans.htm**

Forest Family Forever!

1000-year-old Grandfather Tree shares his knowledge about rainforests' plant and animal life, destruction, and importance to world ecology.

Availability: Schools, libraries, and homeschoolers in the United States who serve the hearing impaired.
Suggested Grade: 2-6
Order Number: 11346
Production Date: 2001
Format: DVD
Special Notes: Also available as live streaming video over the Internet.
Terms: Sponsor pays all transportation costs. Return one week after receipt. Participation is limited to deaf or hard of hearing Americans, their parents, families, teachers, counselors, or others whose use would benefit a deaf or hard of hearing person. Only one person in the audience needs to be hearing impaired. You must register--which is free. These videos are all open-captioned--no special equipment is required for viewing.

Source: Described and Captioned Media Program
National Association of the Deaf
4211 Church Street Ext.
Roebuck, SC 29376
Phone: 1-800-237-6213
Fax: 1-800-538-5636
World Wide Web URL: http://www.dcmp.org

Forests Are More Than Trees

Explains the importance of forests to our lives--not just the trees that grow there.

Availability: Schools, libraries, homeschoolers, and nursing homes in Illinois, Indiana, Iowa, Michigan, Minnesota, Missouri, Ohio, and Wisconsin only.
Suggested Grade: 3-12
Order Number: 1
Production Date: 1988
Format: Set of 80 slides
Special Notes: Sound is provided on audiocassette.
Terms: Return postage is paid by borrower. Book 10-14 days in advance. Return 7 days after showing. Please provide alternate showing date.

Source: U. S. Fish and Wildlife Service
Region 3, Resource Library
3815 American Boulevard
Bloomington, MN 55425
Fax: 1-612-725-3279
Email Address: judy_geck@fws.gov

Forest Stewardship

Children will learn that a forest is made up of many different working parts.

Availability: All requesters
Suggested Grade: K
Order Number: not applicable
Format: Online Lesson Plan

Source: Marguerite Wills
World Wide Web URL:
http://sftrc.cas.psu.edu/LessonPlans/Forestry/
ForestStewardship.html

Forest Wars

Topics covered include responsible use of natural resources, sustainable forestry, endangered species, economic and social values, and forest regulations.

Availability: Schools, libraries, and homeschoolers in the United States and Canada.
Suggested Grade: 6-Adult
Order Number: order by title
Format: VHS videotape
Terms: Borrower pays return postage. Return within 15 to 30 days after receipt via United States mail. Provide alternate showing date.

Source: The Forest Foundation
853 Lincoln Way, Suite 104
Auburn, CA 95603
Phone: 1-866-241-8733
Fax: 1-530-823-1850
World Wide Web URL: http://www.calforestfoundation.org

For More Sun

At Taiwan's top university, a dedicated professor guides his students on a valuable journey from theory to practice to build a solar powered car. This is that story.

Availability: Schools, libraries, and homeschoolers in Colorado, Illinois, Indiana, Iowa, Kansas, Michigan, Minnesota, Missouri, Nebraska, North Dakota, Ohio, South Dakota, and Wisconsin.
Suggested Grade: 7-12
Order Number: order by title
Production Date: 2008
Format: DVD
Special Notes: **May be retained permanently.**

Source: Taipei Economic and Cultural Office in Chicago
Press Division
180 North Stetson Avenue, Suite 5702
Chicago, IL 60601
Phone: 1-312-616-6716
Fax: 1-312-616-1497
World Wide Web URL:
Email Address: teco-chicago@mail.gio.gov.tw

From Streets to Streams: Reducing Pollution from Urban Yards

Discusses how to reduce pollution from urban backyards.

Availability: Schools, libraries, homeschoolers, and nursing homes in Illinois, Indiana, Iowa, Michigan, Minnesota, Missouri, Ohio, and Wisconsin only.
Suggested Grade: 4-12
Order Number: 471
Production Date: 1997
Format: VHS videotape

Indicates an Internet Resource--just enter the URL and instantly access the FREE teaching aid you need!
*All materials listed in this 2010-2011 edition are **BRAND NEW!***

13

Terms: Return postage is paid by borrower. Book 10-14 days in advance. Return 7 days after showing. Please provide alternate showing date.

Source: U. S. Fish and Wildlife Service
Region 3, Resource Library
3815 American Boulevard
Bloomington, MN 55425
Fax: 1-612-725-3279
Email Address: judy_geck@fws.gov

From the Heart of the World

Kogi Indians are convinced that modern culture is destroying the balance of life on earth. They attempt to teach us what they know about nature and the spiritual world.

Availability: Schools, libraries, and nursing homes in the United States.
Suggested Grade: 6-12
Order Number: GELA17-video
Production Date: 1991
Format: VHS videotape
Terms: Borrowers must have a User's Agreement on file with this source--available by mail or via the Internet. Return postage is paid by borrower; return 12 days after showing. Book at least three weeks in advance. All borrowers are limited to a total of ten items per semester.

Source: Latin American Resource Center
Stone Center for Latin American Studies
Tulane University, 100 Jones Hall
New Orleans, LA 70118
Phone: 1-504-862-3143
Fax: 1-504-865-6719
World Wide Web URL:
http://stonecenter.tulane.edu/LARCLLCatalogue.htm
Email Address: crcrts@tulane.edu

Global Warming (Earthbeat Series)

Robert Redford convenes the Sundance Symposium, where top U.S. and Soviet officials meet to discuss ways to combat global warming. The current and long-term impacts of carbon dioxide emissions on the earth are presented along with a look at possible solutions and a clear call to action.

Availability: Schools, libraries, homeschoolers, and nursing homes in Illinois, Indiana, Iowa, Michigan, Minnesota, Missouri, Ohio, and Wisconsin only.
Suggested Grade: 9-12
Order Number: 52
Format: VHS videotape
Terms: Return postage is paid by borrower. Book 10-14 days in advance. Return 7 days after showing. Please provide alternate showing date.

Source: U. S. Fish and Wildlife Service
Region 3, Resource Library
3815 American Boulevard
Bloomington, MN 55425
Fax: 1-612-725-3279
Email Address: judy_geck@fws.gov

Gone With the Waste

Depicts the various solid waste alternatives including source reduction, consumer shopping, collection options, and recycling choices.

Availability: Schools, libraries, and homeschoolers in Connecticut, Maine, Massachusetts, New Hampshire, Rhode Island, and Vermont.
Suggested Grade: 6-12
Order Number: VIS RL23
Production Date: 1992
Format: VHS videotape
Terms: Borrower pays return postage. Return within three weeks of receipt. If the tape you request is available, it will be mailed within 5 business days. If not, you will be notified that this video is already out on loan. No more than three titles may be borrowed by one requestor at a time. No reservations for a specific date will be accepted. It is most efficient to order via the web site.

Source: U. S. Environmental Protection Agency, Region 1
Customer Service Center
One Congress Street, Suite 1100
Boston, MA 02214
World Wide Web URL:
http://yosemite.epa.gov/r1/videolen.nsf/

Goose Music

This tape describes waterfowl restoration efforts around the Chesapeake Bay area. Improved agricultural practices and the North American Waterfowl Management Plan are highlighted.

Availability: Schools, libraries, homeschoolers, and nursing homes in Illinois, Indiana, Iowa, Michigan, Minnesota, Missouri, Ohio, and Wisconsin only.
Suggested Grade: 9-12
Order Number: 73
Format: VHS videotape
Terms: Return postage is paid by borrower. Book 10-14 days in advance. Return 7 days after showing. Please provide alternate showing date.

Source: U. S. Fish and Wildlife Service
Region 3, Resource Library
3815 American Boulevard
Bloomington, MN 55425
Fax: 1-612-725-3279
Email Address: judy_geck@fws.gov

Greenhouse Crisis: The American Concern

How are energy consumption, the greenhouse effect, and global warming related? This program details potential consequences of global warming, and addresses the need for energy efficiency and renewable forms of energy. It highlights specific ways individuals can help to resolve this critical environmental problem.

Availability: Schools, libraries, homeschoolers, and nursing homes in the United States.
Suggested Grade: 5-Adult
Order Number: order by title

Format: VHS videotape
Special Notes: Cleared for TV broadcast.
Terms: Borrower pays return postage. Return the day after scheduled showing, via UPS or Priority Mail, insured for $100.00. Book 4 weeks in advance and include an alternate date. Order should include name of person responsible for handling the video, and complete mailing address. Please mention this Guide when ordering. Tapes may not be duplicated, edited or exhibited for a fee.

Source: Church World Service
Film & Video Library
28606 Phillips Street, P. O. Box 968
Elkhart, IN   46515
Phone: 1-800-297-1516, ext. 338
Fax: 1-574-262-0966
World Wide Web URL: http://www.churchworldservice.org
Email Address: videos@churchworldservice.org

Ground Water Adventure Video, The
Defines ground water and uses a simulated computer game to demonstrate how pollution can occur from various sources.
Availability: Schools, libraries, and homeschoolers in Connecticut, Maine, Massachusetts, New Hampshire, Rhode Island, and Vermont.
Suggested Grade: K-8
Order Number: VID 229
Production Date: 1987
Format: VHS videotape
Terms: Borrower pays return postage. Return within three weeks of receipt. If the tape you request is available, it will be mailed within 5 business days. If not, you will be notified that this video is already out on loan. No more than three titles may be borrowed by one requestor at a time. No reservations for a specific date will be accepted. It is most efficient to order via the web site.

Source: U. S. Environmental Protection Agency, Region 1
Customer Service Center
One Congress Street, Suite 1100
Boston, MA   02214
World Wide Web URL:
http://yosemite.epa.gov/r1/videolen.nsf/

Helping Endangered Species Make Dollars and Sense
See how three Missouri landowners improved their operations and the habitat for endangered species at the same time.
Availability: Schools, libraries, homeschoolers, and nursing homes in Illinois, Indiana, Iowa, Michigan, Minnesota, Missouri, Ohio, and Wisconsin only.
Suggested Grade: 7-12
Order Number: 389
Format: VHS videotape
Terms: Return postage is paid by borrower. Book 10-14 days in advance. Return 7 days after showing. Please provide alternate showing date.

Source: U. S. Fish and Wildlife Service
Region 3, Resource Library
3815 American Boulevard
Bloomington, MN   55425
Email Address: judy_geck@fws.gov

Help Save America's Pearly Mussels
This video reviews the natural history of freshwater mussels focusing on their environmental, aesthetic, scientific, and commercial values. It investigates their decline and efforts to preserve, protect and restore the native mussels.
Availability: Schools, libraries, homeschoolers, and nursing homes in Illinois, Indiana, Iowa, Michigan, Minnesota, Missouri, Ohio, and Wisconsin only.
Suggested Grade: 9-12
Order Number: 412
Format: VHS videotape
Terms: Return postage is paid by borrower. Book 10-14 days in advance. Return 7 days after showing. Please provide alternate showing date.

Source: U. S. Fish and Wildlife Service
Region 3, Resource Library
3815 American Boulevard
Bloomington, MN   55425
Fax: 1-612-725-3279
Email Address: judy_geck@fws.gov

Hiroshima, A New Threat--A-Bomb Water Dedication
A-Bomb Water Dedication is a ritual held at Peace Park in Hiroshima on August 6 each year. Spring and well waters from 16 sites in the city are collected for this ritual, and recently it has been discovered that they are so polluted they are not suitable for drinking. This introduces the important relationship between water and people.
Availability: Schools, libraries and homeschoolers in Alabama, Georgia, North Carolina, South Carolina, and Virginia.
Suggested Grade: 9-Adult
Order Number: 306
Production Date: 1990
Format: VHS videotape
Special Notes: No. 7 of the "Nippon Life" series.
Terms: Borrower pays return postage. Two tapes may be borrowed at a time. Return within 7 days after receipt. Reservations may be made by filling the application found on the web site.

Source: Consulate General of Japan, Atlanta
Japan Information Center
One Alliance Center
3500 Lenox Road, Suite 1600
Atlanta, GA   30326
Phone: 1-404-365-9240
Fax: 1-404-240-4311
World Wide Web URL:
http://www.atlanta.us.emb-japan.go.jp
Email Address: info@cgjapanatlanta.org

Indicates an Internet Resource--just enter the URL and instantly access the FREE teaching aid you need!
All materials listed in this 2010-2011 edition are BRAND NEW!

15

Hiroshima, A New Threat--A-Bomb Water Dedication
A-Bomb Water Dedication is a ritual held at Peace Park in Hiroshima on August 6 each year. Spring and well waters from 16 sites in the city are collected for this ritual, and recently it has been discovered that they are so polluted they are not suitable for drinking. This introduces the important relationship between water and people.

Availability:	Schools, libraries, and nursing homes in Hawaii.
Suggested Grade:	9-Adult
Order Number:	NA-17
Production Date:	1990
Format:	VHS videotape
Special Notes:	No. 7 of the "Nippon Life" series.
Terms:	Borrower pays return postage. A maximum of 3 videos may be borrowed per person. Return within one week of date borrowed.

> **Source: Consulate General of Japan, Honolulu**
> **1742 Nuuanu Avenue**
> **Honolulu, HI 96817-3294**
> **Phone: 1-808-543-3111**
> **Fax: 1-808-543-3170**
> **World Wide Web URL:**
> **http://www.honolulu.us.emb-japan.go.jp**

Hiroshima, A New Threat--A-Bomb Water Dedication
A-Bomb Water Dedication is a ritual held at Peace Park in Hiroshima on August 6 each year. Spring and well waters from 16 sites in the city are collected for this ritual, and recently it has been discovered that they are so polluted they are not suitable for drinking. This introduces the important relationship between water and people.

Availability:	Schools, libraries, homeschoolers, and nursing homes in Nevada and northern California (zip codes beginning 932 and above, except 935).
Suggested Grade:	9-Adult
Order Number:	order by title
Production Date:	1990
Format:	Beta videotape; U-matic videotape; VHS videotape
Special Notes:	No. 7 of the "Nippon Life" series.
Terms:	Borrower pays return postage. Book two weeks in advance. Return within three weeks of date borrowed, via UPS, Federal Express or certified mail.

> **Source: Consulate General of Japan, San Francisco**
> **50 Fremont Street, Suite 2300**
> **San Francisco, CA 94105-2236**
> **Phone: 1-415-356-2564**
> **Fax: 1-415-777-0518**
> **World Wide Web URL: http://www.cgjsf.org/**
> **Email Address: infoav@cgjsf.org**

Hypoxia
Defines hypoxia and discusses its causes, effects, how it develops, and how to protect waters from it.

Availability:	All requesters
Suggested Grade:	6-Adult

Order Number:	not applicable
Format:	Online Fact Sheet

> **Source: Ecological Society of America, The**
> **World Wide Web URL:**
> **http://www.esa.org/education_diversity/factsheets.php**

Jaguar Trax
This video provides an entertaining way of teaching young people the value of tropical rainforests, preserving biodiversity, and sustainably grown products.

Availability:	Schools and libraries in Iowa, Illinois, Michigan, Minnesota, and Wisconsin.
Suggested Grade:	6-12
Order Number:	ENVRFJ18VHS
Format:	VHS videotape
Special Notes:	Includes a study guide.
Terms:	Borrower pays return postage. Return 8 days after showing. Book 2 weeks in advance. Order may also be picked up for those near the Center.

> **Source: Center for Latin American and Caribbean Studies**
> **UW-Milwaukee**
> **P. O. Box 413**
> **Milwaukee, WI 53201**
> **Phone: 1-414-229-5987**
> **World Wide Web URL: http://www.uwm.edu/Dept/CLACS**
> **Email Address: audvis@usm.edu**

Jungle
Development and industrialization of the rain forests.

Availability:	Schools, libraries, and nursing homes in the United States.
Suggested Grade:	6-12
Order Number:	GESA5-video
Format:	VHS videotape
Terms:	Borrowers must have a User's Agreement on file with this source--available by mail or via the Internet. Return postage is paid by borrower; return 12 days after showing. Book at least three weeks in advance. All borrowers are limited to a total of ten items per semester.

> **Source: Latin American Resource Center**
> **Stone Center for Latin American Studies**
> **Tulane University**
> **100 Jones Hall**
> **New Orleans, LA 70118**
> **Phone: 1-504-862-3143**
> **Fax: 1-504-865-6719**
> **World Wide Web URL:**
> **http://stonecenter.tulane.edu/LARCLLCatalogue.htm**
> **Email Address: crcrts@tulane.edu**

Kids by the Bay
Featuring an upbeat score highlighted by the Otis Redding classic "Sittin' on the Dock of the Bay," this video shows how much fun it is to pitch in and restore the environment. From the simple clean-up of trash to the planting of native plants; from island habitat restoration to the rescue and care of wild animals; we see youngsters having a real impact on the natural world around them.

Availability: All requesters through interlibrary loan.
Suggested Grade: 4-Adult
Order Number: 557(276) K5272 1997 VIDEOC
Production Date: 1997
Format: VHS videotape
Terms: These videotapes are available through interlibrary loan only. Simply request the specific video by name and number at your local public library, university library, or company library. The librarian will submit your request using an ALA interlibrary loan form, and the videos will be mailed to your library for your use. Interlibrary loans are limited to two videos at a time. The address listed below is for the ALA loan form only--your librarian must submit requests to this address.

Source: U. S. Geological Survey Library
345 Middlefield Road, MS 955
Menlo Park, CA 94025

Kids for Conservation: Today and Tomorrow; Illinois Birds

This kit contains various lesson plans and materials for educators to teach about birds using multi-disciplined methods.

Availability: Schools, libraries, homeschoolers, and nursing homes in Illinois, Indiana, Iowa, Michigan, Minnesota, Missouri, Ohio, and Wisconsin only.
Suggested Grade: 3-8
Order Number: 2
Format: VHS videotape
Special Notes: Kit includes a poster, activities, and lesson plans.
Terms: Return postage is paid by borrower. Book 10-14 days in advance. Return 7 days after showing. Please provide alternate showing date.

Source: U. S. Fish and Wildlife Service
Region 3, Resource Library
3815 American Boulevard
Bloomington, MN 55425
Fax: 1-612-725-3279
Email Address: judy_geck@fws.gov

Know Your Water Coloring Book

A complete coloring and activity book.

Availability: All requesters
Suggested Grade: K-3
Order Number: not applicable
Format: Downloadable Coloring Book

Source: Texas Water Development Board
World Wide Web URL:
http://www.twdb.state.tx.us/assistance/conservation/pubs.asp

Last Show on Earth Series: Part 2: Endangered Habitat

Author Gerald Durrell and Dr. Ulysses S. Seal tell several success stories including the St. Lucia Parrot and the Florida Panther. Activists Sam LaBudde took pictures on a tuna boat that forced the tuna industry to change its practices and saved millions of dolphins. But for true progress in the war against extinction, we must save both the species and its habitat. Music by Soul II Soul, Seal, David Gilmour, and Peter Gabriel.

Availability: Schools, libraries, homeschoolers, and nursing homes in the United States.
Suggested Grade: 9-Adult
Order Number: order by title
Production Date: 1992
Format: VHS videotape
Terms: Borrower pays return postage. Return the day after scheduled showing, via UPS or Priority Mail, insured for $100.00. Book 4 weeks in advance and include an alternate date. Order should include name of person responsible for handling the video, and complete mailing address. Please mention this Guide when ordering. Tapes may not be duplicated, edited or exhibited for a fee.

Source: Church World Service
Film & Video Library
28606 Phillips Street, P. O. Box 968
Elkhart, IN 46515
Phone: 1-800-297-1516, ext. 338
Fax: 1-574-262-0966
World Wide Web URL: http://www.churchworldservice.org
Email Address: videos@churchworldservice.org

Learning About Acid Rain

This revised guide is designed to help students better understand the science, cause and effect, and regulatory and citizen action that are part of understanding and addressing acid rain.

Availability: All requesters
Suggested Grade: 6-8
Order Number: Not applicable
Format: Downloadable Teacher's Guide
Special Notes: Thi sis a PDF file which will automatically download to your computer.

Source: U. S. Environmental Protection Agency, Acid Rain Program
World Wide Web URL:
http://www.epa.gov/acidrain/education/teachersguide.pdf
Email Address: ordweb.group@epa.gov

Legal Winds of Change: Business and the New Clean Air Act

A conference held November 1990 on the Clean Air Act Amendments' effect on small business. It includes interviews with key Congressional, EPA and local air quality officials.

Availability: Schools, libraries, and homeschoolers in Connecticut, Maine, Massachusetts, New Hampshire, Rhode Island, and Vermont.
Suggested Grade: Adult
Order Number: VID 004
Production Date: 1990
Format: VHS videotape

 Indicates an Internet Resource--just enter the URL and instantly access the FREE teaching aid you need!
All materials listed in this 2010-2011 edition are BRAND NEW!

17

Terms: Borrower pays return postage. Return within three weeks of receipt. If the tape you request is available, it will be mailed within 5 business days. If not, you will be notified that this video is already out on loan. No more than three titles may be borrowed by one requestor at a time. No reservations for a specific date will be accepted. It is most efficient to order via the web site.

Source: U. S. Environmental Protection Agency, Region 1
Customer Service Center
One Congress Street, Suite 1100
Boston, MA 02214
World Wide Web URL:
http://yosemite.epa.gov/r1/videolen.nsf/

Living on the Brink
Explores the devastating loss of species. Using an interactive learning format, live video, games, interviews, and more the site reveals the story in a format and style that allows students to see the real world.

Availability:	All requesters
Suggested Grade:	4-Adult
Order Number:	not applicable
Format:	Web Site
Special Notes:	This URL will lead you to a subject page. Then click on the appropriate subject heading.

Source: ThinkQuest
World Wide Web URL:
http://www.thinkquest.org/pls/html/think.library

Madre Tierra
Nine beautiful animated films from South America, each with its own very special message about the environment and the importance of air, water, and earth.

Availability:	Schools and libraries in Iowa, Illinois, Michigan, Minnesota, and Wisconsin.
Suggested Grade:	4-12
Order Number:	ENVSAM26VHS
Production Date:	1993
Format:	VHS videotape
Special Notes:	No narration.
Terms:	Borrower pays return postage. Return 8 days after showing. Book 2 weeks in advance. Order may also be picked up for those near the Center.

Source: Center for Latin American and Caribbean Studies
UW-Milwaukee
P. O. Box 413
Milwaukee, WI 53201
Phone: 1-414-229-5987
World Wide Web URL: http://www.uwm.edu/Dept/CLACS
Email Address: audvis@usm.edu

1959: Endangered Planet
Presents a historical perspective of the rise of environmental concerns and movements.

Availability:	Schools, libraries, and homeschoolers in the United States who serve the hearing impaired.
Suggested Grade:	9-Adult
Order Number:	13447
Production Date:	1999

Format:	DVD
Terms:	Sponsor pays all transportation costs. Return one week after receipt. Participation is limited to deaf or hard of hearing Americans, their parents, families, teachers, counselors, or others whose use would benefit a deaf or hard of hearing person. Only one person in the audience needs to be hearing impaired. You must register--which is free. These videos are all open-captioned--no special equipment is required for viewing.

Source: Described and Captioned Media Program
National Association of the Deaf
4211 Church Street Ext.
Roebuck, SC 29376
Phone: 1-800-237-6213
Fax: 1-800-538-5636
World Wide Web URL: http://www.dcmp.org

Once Upon a Rainy Day
A rainy day becomes an aqueous adventure for two youngsters when Wally the Water Wizard drops in on them. Their stormy adventures include riding on a cloud, coming face-to-face with a dinosaur, chasing a raindrop, and journeying into the future to see how much we depend on water.

Availability:	Schools, libraries, homeschoolers, and nursing homes in the United States.
Suggested Grade:	K-6
Order Number:	order by title
Production Date:	1981
Format:	VHS videotape
Terms:	Borrower pays return postage. Return the day after scheduled showing, via UPS or Priority Mail, insured for $100.00. Book 4 weeks in advance and include an alternate date. Order should include name of person responsible for handling the video, and complete mailing address. Please mention this Guide when ordering. Tapes may not be duplicated, edited or exhibited for a fee.

Source: Church World Service
Film & Video Library
28606 Phillips Street, P. O. Box 968
Elkhart, IN 46515
Phone: 1-800-297-1516, ext. 338
Fax: 1-574-262-0966
World Wide Web URL: http://www.churchworldservice.org
Email Address: videos@churchworldservice.org

Operation Zap
Chronicles the one-day effort of cleaning up the pollution along the banks of Blackstone River. Shows how political and public relations support is needed for the success of such a project.

Availability:	Schools, libraries, and homeschoolers in Connecticut, Maine, Massachusetts, New Hampshire, Rhode Island, and Vermont.
Suggested Grade:	7-12
Order Number:	VID 007
Production Date:	1974
Format:	VHS videotape

  Indicates an Internet Resource--just enter the URL and instantly access the FREE teaching aid you need!
*All materials listed in this 2010-2011 edition are **BRAND NEW!***

CONSERVATION EDUCATION

Terms: Borrower pays return postage. Return within three weeks of receipt. If the tape you request is available, it will be mailed within 5 business days. If not, you will be notified that this video is already out on loan. No more than three titles may be borrowed by one requestor at a time. No reservations for a specific date will be accepted. It is most efficient to order via the web site.

Source: U. S. Environmental Protection Agency, Region 1
Customer Service Center
One Congress Street, Suite 1100
Boston, MA 02214
World Wide Web URL:
http://yosemite.epa.gov/r1/videolen.nsf/

Our Water, Our Future

Showcases the accomplishments of two Indian tribes--the Pueblo of Acoma located in New Mexico and the Confederated Tribes of the Chehalis Reservation located in Washington--to protect the quality of their waters and the health of their members by adopting water quality standards.

Availability: All requesters through interlibrary loan.
Suggested Grade: 4-12
Order Number: 797(200) 097 2003 VIDEOC
Production Date: 2003
Format: VHS videotape
Terms: These videotapes are available through interlibrary loan only. Simply request the specific video by name and number at your local public library, university library, or company library. The librarian will submit your request using an ALA interlibrary loan form, and the videos will be mailed to your library for your use. Interlibrary loans are limited to two videos at a time. The address listed below is for the ALA loan form only--your librarian must submit requests to this address.

Source: U. S. Geological Survey Library
345 Middlefield Road, MS 955
Menlo Park, CA 94025

Outdoor, Experiential, and Environmental Education: Converging or Diverging Approaches?

Begins with a discussion of definitions relating to these types of education and concludes with examples of combining the approaches to conduct lessons in a variety of content areas.

Availability: All requesters
Suggested Grade: Teacher Reference
Order Number: not applicable
Production Date: 2002
Format: Online Article

Source: C. Adkins and B. Simmons
World Wide Web URL: http://www.ericdigests.org/
2003-2/outdoor.html

Pay As You Throw

Watch residents of Douglass Township, Pennsylvania as they learn how to throw out less waste or pay the price.

Availability: One copy to schools, libraries, and homeschoolers world-wide.
Suggested Grade: 7-Adult
Order Number: 530V98001
Production Date: 2001
Format: VHS videotape
Special Notes: **May be retained permanently.**

Source: U. S. Environmental Protection Agency, NSCEP
P. O. Box 42419
Cincinnati, OH 45242-0419
Phone: 1-800-490-9198
Fax: 1-301-604-3408
World Wide Web URL: http://www.epa.gov/ncepihom/
Email Address: nscep@bps-lmit.com

Please Don't Use Lawn Chemicals

Recording of a presentation on harmful lawn chemicals.

Availability: Schools, libraries, homeschoolers, and nursing homes in Illinois, Indiana, Iowa, Michigan, Minnesota, Missouri, Ohio, and Wisconsin only.
Suggested Grade: 9-Adult
Order Number: 195
Production Date: 1994
Format: VHS videotape
Terms: Return postage is paid by borrower. Book 10-14 days in advance. Return 7 days after showing. Please provide alternate showing date.

Source: U. S. Fish and Wildlife Service
Region 3, Resource Library
3815 American Boulevard
Bloomington, MN 55425
Fax: 1-612-725-3279
Email Address: judy_geck@fws.gov

Pointless Pollution: America's Water Crisis

Focuses on how non-point pollution has affected the lives of people in our country. This source of pollution contributes as much as 80% of the contamination found in our water resources.

Availability: Schools, libraries, homeschoolers, and nursing homes in Illinois, Indiana, Iowa, Michigan, Minnesota, Missouri, Ohio, and Wisconsin only.
Suggested Grade: 9-12
Order Number: 299
Format: VHS videotape
Terms: Return postage is paid by borrower. Book 10-14 days in advance. Return 7 days after showing. Please provide alternate showing date.

Source: U. S. Fish and Wildlife Service
Region 3, Resource Library
3815 American Boulevard
Bloomington, MN 55425
Fax: 1-612-725-3279
Email Address: judy_geck@fws.gov

off
off

Indicates an Internet Resource--just enter the URL and instantly access the FREE teaching aid you need!
All materials listed in this 2010-2011 edition are BRAND NEW!

19

Poisoned Home, Poisoned People: CNN and Time on Special Assignment

Highlights "cotton poison" or methyl-parathion and its illegal use by exterminators inside homes.

Availability: Schools, libraries, and homeschoolers in Connecticut, Maine, Massachusetts, New Hampshire, Rhode Island, and Vermont.
Suggested Grade: 9-Adult
Order Number: VID 231
Production Date: 1997
Format: VHS videotape
Terms: Borrower pays return postage. Return within three weeks of receipt. If the tape you request is available, it will be mailed within 5 business days. If not, you will be notified that this video is already out on loan. No more than three titles may be borrowed by one requestor at a time. No reservations for a specific date will be accepted. It is most efficient to order via the web site.

Source: U. S. Environmental Protection Agency, Region 1
Customer Service Center
One Congress Street, Suite 1100
Boston, MA 02214
World Wide Web URL:
http://yosemite.epa.gov/r1/videolen.nsf/

Pollution Prevention Toolbox

A series of four page lesson plans on various pollution prevention concepts for schools.

Availability: All requesters
Suggested Grade: 2-8
Order Number: not applicable
Format: Online Lesson Plans

Source: U. S. Environmental Protection Agency, Region V
World Wide Web URL:
http://www.epa.gov/reg5rcra/wptdiv/p2pages/toolbox.htm

Preserving Endangered Species: Earthbeat Series

Research suggests that in 25-50 years a quarter of the species of plants and animals existing today will have become extinct. Three segments in this program highlight the difference individuals are making in protecting endangered animals from extinction.

Availability: Schools, libraries, homeschoolers, and nursing homes in Illinois, Indiana, Iowa, Michigan, Minnesota, Missouri, Ohio, and Wisconsin only.
Suggested Grade: 7-12
Order Number: 54
Production Date: 1989
Format: VHS videotape
Terms: Return postage is paid by borrower. Book 10-14 days in advance. Return 7 days after showing. Please provide alternate showing date.

Source: U. S. Fish and Wildlife Service
Region 3, Resource Library
3815 American Boulevard
Bloomington, MN 55425
Fax: 1-612-725-3279
Email Address: judy_geck@fws.gov

Rain Forest Connections

Shows forest destruction in Central and South America, causes, and possible solutions and consequences for Louisiana and the rest of the United States.

Availability: Schools, libraries, and nursing homes in the United States.
Suggested Grade: 6-12
Order Number: GELA7-Video
Production Date: 1985
Format: VHS videotape
Terms: Borrowers must have a User's Agreement on file with this source--available by mail or via the Internet. Return postage is paid by borrower; return 12 days after showing. Book at least three weeks in advance. All borrowers are limited to a total of ten items per semester.

Source: Latin American Resource Center
Stone Center for Latin American Studies
Tulane University
100 Jones Hall
New Orleans, LA 70118
Phone: 1-504-862-3143
Fax: 1-504-865-6719
World Wide Web URL:
http://stonecenter.tulane.edu/LARCLLCatalogue.htm
Email Address: crcrts@tulane.edu

Recycle

Shows the successful recycling program created at Stonington High School in Pawcatuck, Connecticut.

Availability: Schools, libraries, and homeschoolers in Connecticut, Maine, Massachusetts, New Hampshire, Rhode Island, and Vermont.
Suggested Grade: 9-Adult
Order Number: VID 370
Production Date: 2001
Format: VHS videotape
Terms: Borrower pays return postage. Return within three weeks of receipt. If the tape you request is available, it will be mailed within 5 business days. If not, you will be notified that this video is already out on loan. No more than three titles may be borrowed by one requestor at a time. No reservations for a specific date will be accepted. It is most efficient to order via the web site.

Source: U. S. Environmental Protection Agency, Region 1
Customer Service Center
One Congress Street, Suite 1100
Boston, MA 02214
World Wide Web URL:
http://yosemite.epa.gov/r1/videolen.nsf/

Recycle Center, The

An introduction to Boston's recycle center where teachers and parents can obtain manufacturing by-products donated by local businesses at no charge.

Availability: Schools, libraries, and homeschoolers in Connecticut, Maine, Massachusetts, New Hampshire, Rhode Island, and Vermont.
Suggested Grade: 7-Adult
Order Number: VID 271

Format: VHS videotape

Terms: Borrower pays return postage. Return within three weeks of receipt. If the tape you request is available, it will be mailed within 5 business days. If not, you will be notified that this video is already out on loan. No more than three titles may be borrowed by one requestor at a time. No reservations for a specific date will be accepted. It is most efficient to order via the web site.

Source: U. S. Environmental Protection Agency, Region 1
Customer Service Center
One Congress Street, Suite 1100
Boston, MA 02214
World Wide Web URL:
http://yosemite.epa.gov/r1/videolen.nsf/

Recycle This! Rock 'n Roll & Recycling

Set to rock and roll music, this video emphasizes that recycling helps protect the environment, save energy, reduce waste, and conserve resources.

Availability: Schools, libraries, and homeschoolers in Connecticut, Maine, Massachusetts, New Hampshire, Rhode Island, and Vermont.

Suggested Grade: 1-5

Order Number: VID 079

Format: VHS videotape

Special Notes: Produced by the Dow Chemical Company.

Terms: Borrower pays return postage. Return within three weeks of receipt. If the tape you request is available, it will be mailed within 5 business days. If not, you will be notified that this video is already out on loan. No more than three titles may be borrowed by one requestor at a time. No reservations for a specific date will be accepted. It is most efficient to order via the web site.

Source: U. S. Environmental Protection Agency, Region 1
Customer Service Center
One Congress Street, Suite 1100
Boston, MA 02214
World Wide Web URL:
http://yosemite.epa.gov/r1/videolen.nsf/

Recycling

See how the city of Machida in suburban Tokyo, has developed and put into operation a disposal system effective in recycling raw material and reducing sheer volume of daily waste.

Availability: Schools, libraries, homeschoolers, and nursing homes in Connecticut (except Fairfield County), Maine, Massachusetts, New Hampshire, Rhode Island, and Vermont.

Suggested Grade: 6-12

Order Number: 559

Production Date: 1982

Format: VHS videotape

Terms: Borrower pays return postage, including insurance. Return two weeks after receipt.

Source: Consulate General of Japan, Boston
Federal Reserve Plaza, 14th Floor
600 Atlantic Avenue
Boston, MA 02210

Phone: 1-617-973-9772
Fax: 1-617-542-1329
World Wide Web URL:
http://www.boston.us.emb-japan.go.jp
Email Address: infocul@cgjbos.org

Recycling

See how the city of Machida in suburban Tokyo, has developed and put into operation a disposal system effective in recycling raw material and reducing sheer volume of daily waste.

Availability: Schools, libraries, homeschoolers, and nursing homes in Arizona and California (zipcodes beginning 900-931 and 935).

Suggested Grade: 6-12

Order Number: 068

Format: VHS videotape

Terms: Borrower pays postage both ways; you may call the number below to learn how much postage costs. Return within two weeks of date borrowed. An individual may borrow 2 items at one time. For non-profit and educational use only.

Source: Consulate General of Japan, Los Angeles
350 South Grand Avenue, Suite 1700
Los Angeles, CA 90071-3459
Phone: 1-213-617-6700
Fax: 1-213-617-6727
World Wide Web URL: http://www.la.us.emb-japan.go.jp

Recycling Lesson Plan

Students will learn more about recycling.

Availability: All requesters

Suggested Grade: 3

Order Number: not applicable

Format: Online Lesson Plan

Source: Hope Wenzel
World Wide Web URL:
http://sftrc.cas.psu.edu/LessonPlans/Forestry/Recycling.html

Recycling: The Endless Circle

Shows how we can reduce, reuse, and recycle to bring our solid waste problem under control.

Availability: Schools, libraries, homeschoolers, and nursing homes in Illinois, Indiana, Iowa, Michigan, Minnesota, Missouri, Ohio, and Wisconsin only.

Suggested Grade: 9-12

Order Number: 354

Format: VHS videotape

Terms: Return postage is paid by borrower. Book 10-14 days in advance. Return 7 days after showing. Please provide alternate showing date.

Source: U. S. Fish and Wildlife Service
Region 3, Resource Library
3815 American Boulevard
Bloomington, MN 55425
Fax: 1-612-725-3279
Email Address: judy_geck@fws.gov

 Indicates an Internet Resource--just enter the URL and instantly access the FREE teaching aid you need!
All materials listed in this 2010-2011 edition are BRAND NEW!

21

Reduce, Reuse, Recycle: The Bottom Line

Representatives of a few companies teach businesses how to reuse materials, source, and recycle.

Availability: Schools, libraries, and homeschoolers in Connecticut, Maine, Massachusetts, New Hampshire, Rhode Island, and Vermont.

Suggested Grade: 9-Adult
Order Number: VID RL48
Production Date: 1992
Format: VHS videotape

Terms: Borrower pays return postage. Return within three weeks of receipt. If the tape you request is available, it will be mailed within 5 business days. If not, you will be notified that this video is already out on loan. No more than three titles may be borrowed by one requestor at a time. No reservations for a specific date will be accepted. It is most efficient to order via the web site.

Source: U. S. Environmental Protection Agency, Region 1
Customer Service Center
One Congress Street, Suite 1100
Boston, MA 02214
World Wide Web URL:
http://yosemite.epa.gov/r1/videolen.nsf/

Reducing School Bus Idling: The Key to a Healthier Ride

Discusses the benefits of reducing school bus idling--a procedure that saves fuel (money), helps children's health, and prevents air pollution.

Availability: One copy to schools, libraries, and homeschoolers world-wide.

Suggested Grade: 7-Adult
Order Number: 420V04001
Production Date: 2004
Format: VHS videotape
Special Notes: **May be retained permanently.** Closed captioned.

Source: U. S. Environmental Protection Agency, NSCEP
P. O. Box 42419
Cincinnati, OH 45242-0419
Phone: 1-800-490-9198
Fax: 1-301-604-3408
World Wide Web URL: http://www.epa.gov/ncepihom/
Email Address: nscep@bps-lmit.com

Replanting the Tree of Life

A pragmatic but also inspirational look at both trees and forests and what they mean to our lives and well-being. Includes a look at cellular structure and function, the relationships of water, air, and trees, the uses and abuses of forests, and various facets of forestry.

Availability: Schools, libraries, homeschoolers, and nursing homes in Illinois, Indiana, Iowa, Michigan, Minnesota, Missouri, Ohio, and Wisconsin only.

Suggested Grade: 9-12
Order Number: 130
Format: VHS videotape

Terms: Return postage is paid by borrower. Book 10-14 days in advance. Return 7 days after showing. Please provide alternate showing date.

Source: U. S. Fish and Wildlife Service
Region 3, Resource Library
3815 American Boulevard
Bloomington, MN 55425
Fax: 1-612-725-3279
Email Address: judy_geck@fws.gov

Reviving Our Rain Forests--The Mission of Professor Akira Miyawaki

Professor Miyawaki was instrumental in developing a personal reforestation program in Japan; here is an interview with him.

Availability: Schools, libraries, and nursing homes in Hawaii.

Suggested Grade: 6-12
Order Number: NA-4
Production Date: 1992
Format: VHS videotape

Terms: Borrower pays return postage. A maximum of 3 videos may be borrowed per person. Return within one week of date borrowed.

Source: Consulate General of Japan, Honolulu
1742 Nuuanu Avenue
Honolulu, HI 96817-3294
Phone: 1-808-543-3111
Fax: 1-808-543-3170
World Wide Web URL:
http://www.honolulu.us.emb-japan.go.jp

Reviving Our Rain Forests--The Mission of Professor Akira Miyawaki

Professor Miyawaki was instrumental in developing a personal reforestation program in Japan; here is an interview with him.

Availability: Schools, libraries, homeschoolers, and nursing homes in Arizona and California (zipcodes beginning 900-931 and 935).

Suggested Grade: 6-12
Order Number: 194
Production Date: 1992
Format: VHS videotape

Terms: Borrower pays postage both ways; you may call the number below to learn how much postage costs. Return within two weeks of date borrowed. An individual may borrow 2 items at one time. For non-profit and educational use only.

Source: Consulate General of Japan, Los Angeles
350 South Grand Avenue, Suite 1700
Los Angeles, CA 90071-3459
Phone: 1-213-617-6700
Fax: 1-213-617-6727
World Wide Web URL: http://www.la.us.emb-japan.go.jp

Reviving Our Rain Forests--The Mission of Professor Akira Miyawaki

Professor Miyawaki was instrumental in developing a

personal reforestation program in Japan; here is an interview with him.

Availability:	Schools, libraries, homeschoolers, and nursing homes in OREGON AND SOUTHERN IDAHO ONLY. Please make requests via the web site.
Suggested Grade:	6-12
Order Number:	194
Production Date:	1992
Format:	VHS videotape
Terms:	Borrower pays return postage. Return within three weeks after scheduled showing date. Book one month in advance if possible. Rewind the video and wrap securely for return. Be certain to indicate video number, date needed, name of your organization, and address to which video should be sent, along with phone number. Audience report enclosed with the video must be completed and returned.

Source: Consulate General of Japan, Oregon
Attn: Tamara, Video Library
1300 S. W. Fifth Avenue, Suite 2700
Portland, OR 97201
Phone: 1-503-221-1811, ext. 17
World Wide Web URL:
http://www.portland.us.emb-japan.go.jp/en/index.html
Email Address: tamara@cgjpdx.org

Roll On, Manatee

One of the most loved, and sadly, one of the most endangered animals of the world, is the West Indian Manatee. This National Education Film Festival award winner, offers a close-up look at these amazing animals and the many human-related dangers that now threaten their survival.

Availability:	Schools, libraries, homeschoolers, and nursing homes in Illinois, Indiana, Iowa, Michigan, Minnesota, Missouri, Ohio, and Wisconsin only.
Suggested Grade:	K-12
Order Number:	81
Format:	VHS videotape
Terms:	Return postage is paid by borrower. Book 10-14 days in advance. Return 7 days after showing. Please provide alternate showing date.

Source: U. S. Fish and Wildlife Service
Region 3, Resource Library
3815 American Boulevard
Bloomington, MN 55425
Fax: 1-612-725-3279
Email Address: judy_geck@fws.gov

Rotten Truth, The

The PBS series "3-2-1 Contact" takes viewers on a visit to the fictitious "Museum of Modern Garbage" and to landfill sites to dramatize the mounting waste problem, and the need for consumers to change their habits.

Availability:	Schools, libraries, and homeschoolers in Connecticut, Maine, Massachusetts, New Hampshire, Rhode Island, and Vermont.

Suggested Grade:	All ages
Order Number:	VID 130
Production Date:	1990
Format:	VHS videotape
Terms:	Borrower pays return postage. Return within three weeks of receipt. If the tape you request is available, it will be mailed within 5 business days. If not, you will be notified that this video is already out on loan. No more than three titles may be borrowed by one requestor at a time. No reservations for a specific date will be accepted. It is most efficient to order via the web site.

Source: U. S. Environmental Protection Agency, Region 1
Customer Service Center
One Congress Street, Suite 1100
Boston, MA 02214
World Wide Web URL:
http://yosemite.epa.gov/r1/videolen.nsf/

Save the Rainforest

Provides a virtual tour of the rainforest and lots of information about why we need them and why they are becoming endangered ecosystems.

Availability:	All requesters
Suggested Grade:	All ages
Order Number:	not applicable
Format:	Web Site

Source: Save the Rainforest.org
World Wide Web URL: http://www.savetherainforest.org/

Saving Endangered Species

Tells about the nation's Endangered Species Act. This is for anyone who wants to make a difference-for wildlife, the environment, and a healthier world.

Availability:	Schools, libraries, homeschoolers, and nursing homes in Illinois, Indiana, Iowa, Michigan, Minnesota, Missouri, Ohio, and Wisconsin only.
Suggested Grade:	9-12
Order Number:	367
Format:	VHS videotape
Terms:	Return postage is paid by borrower. Book 10-14 days in advance. Return 7 days after showing. Please provide alternate showing date.

Source: U. S. Fish and Wildlife Service
Region 3, Resource Library
3815 American Boulevard
Bloomington, MN 55425
Fax: 1-612-725-3279
Email Address: judy_geck@fws.gov

Saving Polluterville: An Ocean Pollution Investigation

Discover the impact of pollution on the ocean and explore some solutions.

Availability:	All requesters
Suggested Grade:	5
Order Number:	not applicable
Format:	WebQuest

 Indicates an Internet Resource--just enter the URL and instantly access the FREE teaching aid you need!
All materials listed in this 2010-2011 edition are BRAND NEW!

23

Source: Kalie Dalferes, Brittany Schilling, and Clare Tupper
World Wide Web URL:
http://oncampus.richmond.edu/academics/education/projects/webquests/oceans/

Serpent Fruits

Traces the effects of chemicals on the environment and on living creatures. Goes through an explanation of how chemicals are tested to see if they are carcinogenic.

Availability: Schools, libraries, and homeschoolers in Connecticut, Maine, Massachusetts, New Hampshire, Rhode Island, and Vermont.
Suggested Grade: 7-Adult
Order Number: VID 014
Production Date: 1979
Format: VHS videotape
Terms: Borrower pays return postage. Return within three weeks of receipt. If the tape you request is available, it will be mailed within 5 business days. If not, you will be notified that this video is already out on loan. No more than three titles may be borrowed by one requestor at a time. No reservations for a specific date will be accepted. It is most efficient to order via the web site.
Source: U. S. Environmental Protection Agency, Region 1
Customer Service Center
One Congress Street, Suite 1100
Boston, MA 02214
World Wide Web URL:
http://yosemite.epa.gov/r1/videolen.nsf/

Single-Use Foodservice Packaging--Facts and Fun Teacher's Kit

A curriculum to help students learn about the benefits of foodservice disposable products.

Availability: All requesters
Suggested Grade: 6-9
Order Number: not applicable
Format: Downloadable Teacher's Kit
Special Notes: Includes lesson plans, activities, glossary, and a new interactive game. May also be downloaded from web site.
Source: Foodservice Packaging Institute, Inc.
World Wide Web URL:
http://www.fpi.org/dms/dm_browse.asp?pid=97

S.O.S. for America's Streams: A Guide to Water Quality Monitoring

Provides a hands-on demonstration of the stream monitoring technique including: stream pollution problems, stream sampling, identification of stream organisms, use of the stream survey, and information on how to adapt a stream and become its active guardian.

Availability: Schools, libraries, homeschoolers, and nursing homes in Illinois, Indiana, Iowa, Michigan, Minnesota, Missouri, Ohio, and Wisconsin only.
Suggested Grade: 9-12

Order Number: 148
Format: VHS videotape
Terms: Return postage is paid by borrower. Book 10-14 days in advance. Return 7 days after showing. Please provide alternate showing date.
Source: U. S. Fish and Wildlife Service
Region 3, Resource Library
3815 American Boulevard
Bloomington, MN 55425
Fax: 1-612-725-3279
Email Address: judy_geck@fws.gov

Special Report: You Can Make a Difference

Shows what each of us can do to protect our environment. You will see how young people work with business leaders, elected officials, parents, and teachers to: cut waste, reduce toxins, save energy, clear the air and protect wildlife.

Availability: Schools, libraries, homeschoolers, and nursing homes in Illinois, Indiana, Iowa, Michigan, Minnesota, Missouri, Ohio, and Wisconsin only.
Suggested Grade: 6-12
Order Number: 326
Format: VHS videotape
Terms: Return postage is paid by borrower. Book 10-14 days in advance. Return 7 days after showing. Please provide alternate showing date.
Source: U. S. Fish and Wildlife Service
Region 3, Resource Library
3815 American Boulevard
Bloomington, MN 55425
Fax: 1-612-725-3279
Email Address: judy_geck@fws.gov

Stepan Chemical: The Poisoning of a Mexican Community

A moving account of the people of Matamoros, Mexico, and their struggle for a clean environment. The Chicago-based Stepan plant has dumped xylene, a toxic solvent linked to birth defects, into open canals near their homes. Faced with this deadly pollution, the Sanchez family and their neighbors decide to fight back. With help from the U. S. based Coalition for Justice in the Maguiladoras, community leaders demand an end to the contamination and a full accounting from Stepan and environmental agencies in the U. S. and Mexico.

Availability: Schools, libraries, homeschoolers, and nursing homes in the United States.
Suggested Grade: 9-Adult
Order Number: order by title
Production Date: 1992
Format: VHS videotape
Terms: Borrower pays return postage. Return the day after scheduled showing, via UPS or Priority Mail, insured for $100.00. Book 4 weeks in advance and include an alternate date. Order should include name of person responsible for handling the video, and complete mailing address. Please mention this Guide when

ordering. Tapes may not be duplicated, edited
or
exhibited for a fee.

Source: Church World Service
Film & Video Library
28606 Phillips Street, P. O. Box 968
Elkhart, IN 46515
Phone: 1-800-297-1516, ext. 338
Fax: 1-574-262-0966
World Wide Web URL: http://www.churchworldservice.org
Email Address: videos@churchworldservice.org

Storm Drain Stenciling Instruction Cards

Designed to improve the quality of our ocean waters
through reduction of pointless pollution and develop
leadership among the participants in the campaign.
Instructions how to organize a local storm drain stenciling
campaign.

Availability: Single copies to schools, libraries, and
                       homeschoolers world-wide.
Suggested Grade: 3-12
Order Number: order by title
Format: Cards

Source: Clean Ocean Action
18 Hartshorne Drive, Suite 2
Sandy Hook, NJ 07732
Phone: 1-732-872-0111
Fax: 1-732-872-8041
World Wide Web URL: http://www.cleanoceanaction.org
Email Address: education@cleanoceanaction.org

Striper! Restoring Coastal Striped Bass

Once the Striped Bass was a major product in the fishing
industry and a popular sport fish. However, the population
of this fish had declined. This video shows how these rivers
are being cleaned up and how fish hatcheries restock these
areas.

Availability: Schools, libraries, homeschoolers, and
                       nursing homes in Illinois, Indiana, Iowa,
                       Michigan, Minnesota, Missouri, Ohio, and
                       Wisconsin only.
Suggested Grade: 9-12
Order Number: 151
Format: VHS videotape
Terms: Return postage is paid by borrower. Book 10-14 days in
          advance. Return 7 days after showing. Please provide
          alternate showing date.

Source: U. S. Fish and Wildlife Service
Region 3, Resource Library
3815 American Boulevard
Bloomington, MN 55425
Fax: 1-612-725-3279
Email Address: judy_geck@fws.gov

Sustainability

Explores the concept of sustainability; how it impacts our
current lives and how it will affect the future. We explore
how we, as a world people, are involved in practices that are
not sustainable.

Availability: All requesters
Suggested Grade: 6-Adult
Order Number: not applicable
Format: Web Site
Special Notes: This URL will lead you to a subject page.
                       Then click on the appropriate subject heading.

Source: ThinkQuest
World Wide Web URL:
http://www.thinkquest.org/pls/html/think.library

Surface Water Video, The

Kid reports explain non-point source pollution and the need
to reduce pollution and water use. The video also offers
some simple ways children can help.

Availability: Schools, libraries, and homeschoolers in
                       Connecticut, Maine, Massachusetts, New
                       Hampshire, Rhode Island, and Vermont.
Suggested Grade: K-6
Order Number: VID 227
Production Date: 1989
Format: VHS videotape
Terms: Borrower pays return postage. Return within three
          weeks of receipt. If the tape you request is available, it
          will be mailed within 5 business days. If not, you will
          be notified that this video is already out on loan. No
          more than three titles may be borrowed by one requestor
          at a time. No reservations for a specific date will be
          accepted. It is most efficient to order via the web site.

Source: U. S. Environmental Protection Agency, Region 1
Customer Service Center
One Congress Street, Suite 1100
Boston, MA 02214
World Wide Web URL:
http://yosemite.epa.gov/r1/videolen.nsf/

Take Pride in America

This program is narrated by Lou Gossett, Jr. It seeks the
American people's help in reducing litter, vandalism, and
other destructive behavior in and around the National Parks
and public lands.

Availability: Schools, libraries, homeschoolers, nursing
                       homes, and others in the United States and
                       Canada.
Suggested Grade: 5-12
Order Number: order by title
Format: VHS videotape
Special Notes: May be copied for permanent retention.
                       Cleared for TV broadcast with advance
                       permission.
Terms: Borrowers pay return postage. Return 30 days after
          scheduled showing, via U.S. Mail. Book 30 days in
          advance. Up to 2 videos will be sent out to one
          customer at a time. Your next order will be mailed as
          soon as you return previously borrowed tapes.

Source: Bureau of Reclamation
U.S. Department of the Interior
Attn: Kristi Thompson, Library, 84-21320
6th Avenue & Kipling Street, Building 67

 Indicates an Internet Resource--just enter the URL and instantly access the FREE teaching aid you need!
All materials listed in this 2010-2011 edition are BRAND NEW!

25

Berntsen Library | Northwestern College

Denver, CO 80225-0007
Phone: 1-303-445-2039
Fax: 1-303-445-6303
World Wide Web URL: http://www.usbr.gov/library
Email Address: library@do.usbr.gov

Take Pride in America--A Legacy of Caring

This documentary describes the Secretary of the Interior's program to reduce litter, vandalism, etc. in and around the National Parks and public lands.

Availability:	Schools, libraries, homeschoolers, nursing homes, and others in the United States and Canada.
Suggested Grade:	5-12
Order Number:	order by title
Production Date:	1989
Format:	VHS videotape
Special Notes:	May be copied for permanent retention. Cleared for TV broadcast with advance permission.
Terms:	Borrowers pay return postage. Return 30 days after scheduled showing, via U.S. Mail. Book 30 days in advance. Up to 2 videos will be sent out to one customer at a time. Your next order will be mailed as soon as you return previously borrowed tapes.

Source: Bureau of Reclamation
U.S. Department of the Interior
Attn: Kristi Thompson, Library, 84-21320
6th Avenue & Kipling Street, Building 67
Denver, CO 80225-0007
Phone: 1-303-445-2039
Fax: 1-303-445-6303
World Wide Web URL: http://www.usbr.gov/library
Email Address: library@do.usbr.gov

Talk About Trees

Activities, lesson plans, newsletters, and more about trees. Availability: All requesters
Suggested Grade: All ages
Order Number: not applicable
Format: Online Lesson Plans and activities

Source: California Women in Timber
World Wide Web URL: http://www.talkabouttrees.org/

10 Tips for Kids

Provides ten ways kids can be a part of the solution to preventing pollution.

Availability:	Single copies to schools, libraries, and homeschoolers world-wide.
Suggested Grade:	3-12
Order Number:	order by title
Format:	Card

Source: Clean Ocean Action
18 Hartshorne Drive, Suite 2
Sandy Hook, NJ 07732
Phone: 1-732-872-0111
Fax: 1-732-872-8041
World Wide Web URL: http://www.cleanoceanaction.org
Email Address: education@cleanoceanaction.org

Top Water Smart Tips

Top conservation tips for the bathroom, kitchen, and outdoors.

Availability:	All requesters
Suggested Grade:	6-Adult
Languages:	English; Spanish
Order Number:	not applicable
Format:	Downloadable Brochure

Source: Texas Water Development Board
World Wide Web URL:
http://www.twdb.state.tx.us/assistance/conservation/pubs.asp

Trouble With Toxins

This video provides a very balanced view of the toxins issue in the Great Lakes ecosystem.

Availability:	Schools, libraries, homeschoolers, and nursing homes in Illinois, Indiana, Iowa, Michigan, Minnesota, Missouri, Ohio, and Wisconsin only.
Suggested Grade:	9-12
Order Number:	154
Format:	VHS videotape
Terms:	Return postage is paid by borrower. Book 10-14 days in advance. Return 7 days after showing. Please provide alternate showing date.

Source: U. S. Fish and Wildlife Service
Region 3, Resource Library
3815 American Boulevard
Bloomington, MN 55425
Fax: 1-612-725-3279
Email Address: judy_geck@fws.gov

Two Sides of Fire

Allows students to discover how the forces of nature help shape forest ecosystems. Explores the benefits of natural fires while also discussing the perils of wildlife.

Availability:	Schools, libraries, and homeschoolers in the United States and Canada.
Suggested Grade:	6-12
Order Number:	order by title
Format:	VHS videotape
Terms:	Borrower pays return postage. Return within 15 to 30 days after receipt via United States mail. Provide alternate showing date.

Source: The Forest Foundation
853 Lincoln Way, Suite 104
Auburn, CA 95603
Phone: 1-866-241-8733
Fax: 1-530-823-1850
World Wide Web URL: http://www.calforestfoundation.org

User's Guide to the Planet Earth, A: The American Environmental Test

Tom Selleck hosts this video that quizzes viewers on their environmental awareness. Celebrities ask a variety of questions regarding land, air, water, and energy issues, then explain the answers.

Availability: Schools, libraries, and homeschoolers in Connecticut, Maine, Massachusetts, New Hampshire, Rhode Island, and Vermont.
Suggested Grade: 7-Adult
Order Number: VID 037
Format: VHS videotape
Terms: Borrower pays return postage. Return within three weeks of receipt. If the tape you request is available, it will be mailed within 5 business days. If not, you will be notified that this video is already out on loan. No more than three titles may be borrowed by one requestor at a time. No reservations for a specific date will be accepted. It is most efficient to order via the web site.
Source: U. S. Environmental Protection Agency, Region 1
Customer Service Center
One Congress Street, Suite 1100
Boston, MA 02214
World Wide Web URL:
http://yosemite.epa.gov/r1/videolen.nsf/

Wasting of a Wetland

This video explores how population, agriculture, and pollution have critically endangered the Florida Everglades.
Availability: Schools, libraries, homeschoolers, and nursing homes in Illinois, Indiana, Iowa, Michigan, Minnesota, Missouri, Ohio, and Wisconsin only.
Suggested Grade: 7-Adult
Order Number: 159
Production Date: 1990
Format: VHS videotape
Terms: Return postage is paid by borrower. Book 10-14 days in advance. Return 7 days after showing. Please provide alternate showing date.
Source: U. S. Fish and Wildlife Service
Region 3, Resource Library
3815 American Boulevard
Bloomington, MN 55425
Fax: 1-612-725-3279
Email Address: judy_geck@fws.gov

Water: A Treasure in Trouble

Shows why water is one of our greatest treasures, how pollution threatens our water supply, and what we can do to safeguard our sources of pure water.
Availability: Schools, libraries, homeschoolers, and nursing homes in the United States.
Suggested Grade: All ages
Order Number: order by title
Format: VHS videotape
Terms: Borrower pays return postage. Return the day after scheduled showing, via UPS or Priority Mail, insured for $100.00. Book 4 weeks in advance and include an alternate date. Order should include name of person responsible for handling the video, and complete mailing address. Please mention this Guide when ordering. Tapes may not be duplicated, edited or exhibited for a fee.

Source: Church World Service
Film & Video Library
28606 Phillips Street, P. O. Box 968
Elkhart, IN 46515
Phone: 1-800-297-1516, ext. 338
Fax: 1-574-262-0966
World Wide Web URL: http://www.churchworldservice.org
Email Address: videos@churchworldservice.org

Water Conservation Lesson Plan

Students will learn the importance of water in everyday living, how we use it, and how to conserve it.
Availability: All requesters
Suggested Grade: 3
Order Number: not applicable
Format: Online Lesson Plan
Source: Hope Wenzel
World Wide Web URL:
http://sftrc.cas.psu.edu/LessonPlans/Water/
WaterConservation.html

Water (Earthbeat Series)

Presents a disturbing look at a number of instances of water contamination.
Availability: Schools, libraries, homeschoolers, and nursing homes in Illinois, Indiana, Iowa, Michigan, Minnesota, Missouri, Ohio, and Wisconsin only.
Suggested Grade: 9-12
Order Number: 53
Format: VHS videotape
Terms: Return postage is paid by borrower. Book 10-14 days in advance. Return 7 days after showing. Please provide alternate showing date.
Source: U. S. Fish and Wildlife Service
Region 3, Resource Library
3815 American Boulevard
Bloomington, MN 55425
Fax: 1-612-725-3279
Email Address: judy_geck@fws.gov

Waterfowl for the Future

Describes the reasons for the recent decline in the waterfowl population and how the North American Waterfowl Management Plan will help to remedy these problems and increase waterfowl population.
Availability: Schools, libraries, homeschoolers, and nursing homes in Illinois, Indiana, Iowa, Michigan, Minnesota, Missouri, Ohio, and Wisconsin only.
Suggested Grade: 5-12
Order Number: 201
Format: VHS videotape
Terms: Return postage is paid by borrower. Book 10-14 days in advance. Return 7 days after showing. Please provide alternate showing date.
Source: U. S. Fish and Wildlife Service
Region 3, Resource Library, 3815 American Boulevard
Bloomington, MN 55425

Indicates an Internet Resource--just enter the URL and instantly access the FREE teaching aid you need!
All materials listed in this 2010-2011 edition are BRAND NEW!

CONSERVATION EDUCATION

Fax: 1-612-725-3279
Email Address: judy_geck@fws.gov

Water on Tap: A Consumer's Guide to the Nation's Drinking Water
Explains where our water comes from and how it's treated. Also explains what sources contaminate water and what to do if your water supply is contaminated.

Availability:	All requesters
Suggested Grade:	4-Adult
Order Number:	not applicable
Format:	Online Article; 22 pages
Special Notes:	Use the on-site search engine to easily find this title. You may request a printed copy mailed to you for a fee.

Source: Federal Citizen Information Center
World Wide Web URL: http://www.pueblo.gsa.gov/

Waterways: Links to the Sea
Information and activities on how to preserve our water resources.

Availability:	Classroom quantities to schools, libraries, and homeschoolers in the United States and Canada.
Suggested Grade:	3-5
Order Number:	order by title
Format:	Activity Guide

Source: Maine Coastal Program
38 State House Station
Augusta, ME 04333
Phone: 1-207-287-1486
Fax: 1-207-287-8059
World Wide Web URL:
http://www.mainecoastalprogram.org
Email Address: lorraine.lessard@maine.gov

We All Live Downstream
The video explores the problems and the stories of people who live along the Mississippi River, many of whom are now fighting to save the Mighty Mississippi.

Availability:	Schools, libraries, homeschoolers, and nursing homes in Illinois, Indiana, Iowa, Michigan, Minnesota, Missouri, Ohio, and Wisconsin only.
Suggested Grade:	5-12
Order Number:	341
Format:	VHS videotape
Terms:	Return postage is paid by borrower. Book 10-14 days in advance. Return 7 days after showing. Please provide alternate showing date.

Source: U. S. Fish and Wildlife Service
Region 3, Resource Library
3815 American Boulevard
Bloomington, MN 55425
Fax: 1-612-725-3279
Email Address: judy_geck@fws.gov

Wetlands: How to Make a Difference
This video teaches strategies and skills for protecting wetlands. Meet people who are fighting for the wetlands and succeeding.

Availability:	Schools, libraries, homeschoolers, and nursing homes in Illinois, Indiana, Iowa, Michigan, Minnesota, Missouri, Ohio, and Wisconsin only.
Suggested Grade:	6-12
Order Number:	248
Format:	VHS videotape
Terms:	Return postage is paid by borrower. Book 10-14 days in advance. Return 7 days after showing. Please provide alternate showing date.

Source: U. S. Fish and Wildlife Service
Region 3, Resource Library
3815 American Boulevard
Bloomington, MN 55425
Fax: 1-612-725-3279
Email Address: judy_geck@fws.gov

Wetlands Regained
The Bureau of Reclamation participates in the restoration and preservation of wetlands. This program describes their participation.

Availability:	Schools, libraries, homeschoolers, nursing homes, and others in the United States and Canada.
Suggested Grade:	5-12
Order Number:	order by title
Production Date:	1991
Format:	VHS videotape
Special Notes:	May be copied for permanent retention. Cleared for TV broadcast with advance permission.
Terms:	Borrowers pay return postage. Return 30 days after scheduled showing, via U.S. Mail. Book 30 days in advance. Up to 2 videos will be sent out to one customer at a time. Your next order will be mailed as soon as you return previously borrowed tapes.

Source: Bureau of Reclamation
U.S. Department of the Interior
Attn: Kristi Thompson, Library, 84-21320
6th Avenue & Kipling Street, Building 67
Denver, CO 80225-0007
Phone: 1-303-445-2039
Fax: 1-303-445-6303
World Wide Web URL: http://www.usbr.gov/library
Email Address: library@do.usbr.gov

What Does Ecology Have to Do with Me?
Presents an introduction to the science of ecology and its role in human society.

Availability:	One copy to schools, libraries, and homeschoolers world-wide.
Suggested Grade:	6-Adult
Order Number:	not applicable
Format:	Online Fact Sheet

Indicates an Internet Resource--just enter the URL and instantly access the FREE teaching aid you need!
All materials listed in this 2010-2011 edition are BRAND NEW!

Special Notes: Single print copies may be mailed to requester.

**Source: Ecological Society of America, The
World Wide Web URL:
http://www.esa.org/education_diversity/webDocs/
ecologyANDme.php**

Whose Woods Are These?

Examination of the pattern of destruction in forests abroad and in the United States.

Availability: Schools, libraries, and nursing homes in the United States.
Suggested Grade: 6-12
Order Number: GE10-video
Production Date: 1992
Format: VHS videotape
Terms: Borrowers must have a User's Agreement on file with this source--available by mail or via the Internet. Return postage is paid by borrower; return 12 days after showing. Book at least three weeks in advance. All borrowers are limited to a total of ten items per semester.

**Source: Latin American Resource Center
Stone Center for Latin American Studies
Tulane University, 100 Jones Hall
New Orleans, LA 70118
Phone: 1-504-862-3143
Fax: 1-504-865-6719
World Wide Web URL:
http://stonecenter.tulane.edu/LARCLLCatalogue.htm
Email Address: crcrts@tulane.edu**

Wild About Life!

A docu-drama about four teenagers who discover the value of the variety of life on earth, from wolves to plants and wetlands to deserts, and are inspired by positive actions to safeguard. Divided into four parts.

Availability: Schools, libraries, homeschoolers, and nursing homes in Illinois, Indiana, Iowa, Michigan, Minnesota, Missouri, Ohio, and Wisconsin only.
Suggested Grade: 6-12
Order Number: 472
Production Date: 1998
Format: VHS videotape
Terms: Return postage is paid by borrower. Book 10-14 days in advance. Return 7 days after showing. Please provide alternate showing date.

**Source: U. S. Fish and Wildlife Service
Region 3, Resource Library
3815 American Boulevard
Bloomington, MN 55425
Fax: 1-612-725-3279
Email Address: judy_geck@fws.gov**

Wildlife Habitat and the Hunter

Explains the importance of wildlife habitat and the effects of habitat change. Shows how man can live in harmony with wildlife. Combines animated characters with a variety of hunting scenes and wildlife footage.

Availability: Schools, libraries, homeschoolers, and nursing homes in Illinois, Indiana, Iowa, Michigan, Minnesota, Missouri, Ohio, and Wisconsin only.
Suggested Grade: 4-12
Order Number: 173
Format: VHS videotape
Terms: Return postage is paid by borrower. Book 10-14 days in advance. Return 7 days after showing. Please provide alternate showing date.

**Source: U. S. Fish and Wildlife Service
Region 3, Resource Library
3815 American Boulevard
Bloomington, MN 55425
Fax: 1-612-725-3279
Email Address: judy_geck@fws.gov**

World Heritage--Shirakami Forest 1997

UNESCO certified Shirakami Mountain Forest, which borders Aomori and Akita prefectures, as a world heritage. This 17,000 hectacre forest area is among nature's most priceless treasures--a heritage that must be preserved for future generations.

Availability: Schools, libraries, homeschoolers, and nursing homes in Connecticut (except Fairfield County), Maine, Massachusetts, New Hampshire, Rhode Island, and Vermont.
Suggested Grade: 6-12
Order Number: 556
Format: VHS videotape
Terms: Borrower pays return postage, including insurance. Return two weeks after receipt.

**Source: Consulate General of Japan, Boston
Federal Reserve Plaza, 14th Floor
600 Atlantic Avenue
Boston, MA 02210
Phone: 1-617-973-9772
Fax: 1-617-542-1329
World Wide Web URL:
http://www.boston.us.emb-japan.go.jp
Email Address: infocul@cgjbos.org**

World Heritage--Shirakami Forest 1997

UNESCO certified Shirakami Mountain Forest, which borders Aomori and Akita prefectures, as a world heritage. This 17,000 hectacre forest area is among nature's most priceless treasures--a heritage that must be preserved for future generations.

Availability: Schools, libraries, and nursing homes in Hawaii.
Suggested Grade: 6-12
Order Number: NA-28
Format: VHS videotape
Terms: Borrower pays return postage. A maximum of 3 videos may be borrowed per person. Return within one week of date borrowed.

**Source: Consulate General of Japan, Honolulu
1742 Nuuanu Avenue
Honolulu, HI 96817-3294**

 Indicates an Internet Resource--just enter the URL and instantly access the FREE teaching aid you need!
*All materials listed in this 2010-2011 edition are **BRAND NEW!***

Phone: 1-808-543-3111
Fax: 1-808-543-3170
World Wide Web URL:
http://www.honolulu.us.emb-japan.go.jp

Wyland Clean Water Challenge

Provides art and science curriculum materials that teach us the importance of water.

Availability:	All requesters
Suggested Grade:	K-6; 7-12
Languages:	English; Spanish
Order Number:	not applicable
Format:	Downloadable Curriculum

Source: Scripps Institution of Oceanography
World Wide Web URL:
http://www.wylandoceanchallenge.org/

You Can't Grow Home Again

Pre-teen takes viewers on a trip to the Costa Rican rainforest to examine issues of preservation.

Availability:	Schools and libraries in Iowa, Illinois, Michigan, Minnesota, and Wisconsin.
Suggested Grade:	6-12
Order Number:	ENVRFY8VHS
Production Date:	1990
Format:	VHS videotape
Terms:	Borrower pays return postage. Return 8 days after showing. Book 2 weeks in advance. Order may also be picked up for those near the Center.

Source: Center for Latin American and Caribbean Studies
UW-Milwaukee
P. O. Box 413
Milwaukee, WI 53201
Phone: 1-414-229-5987
World Wide Web URL: http://www.uwm.edu/Dept/CLACS
Email Address: audvis@usm.edu

Your Car and Clean Air: What you Can Do to Reduce Pollution

Information on your can help keep the air clean and still drive a car.

Availability:	One copy to schools, libraries, and homeschoolers world-wide.
Suggested Grade:	10-Adult
Order Number:	420F94005
Format:	Article

Source: U. S. Environmental Protection Agency, NSCEP
P. O. Box 42419
Cincinnati, OH 45242-2419
Phone: 1-800-490-9198
Fax: 1-301-604-3408
World Wide Web URL:
http://www.epa.gov/ncepihom/orderpub.html
Email Address: nscep@bps-lmit.com

Your Water, Your Life

Delivers a message: grassroots activism works! Alerts citizens to the problems of groundwater contamination and how they can change local policy and improve the environmental health of their communities.

Availability:	Schools, libraries, and homeschoolers in Connecticut, Maine, Massachusetts, New Hampshire, Rhode Island, and Vermont.
Suggested Grade:	9-12
Order Number:	VID 112
Production Date:	1998
Format:	VHS videotape
Terms:	Borrower pays return postage. Return within three weeks of receipt. If the tape you request is available, it will be mailed within 5 business days. If not, you will be notified that this video is already out on loan. No more than three titles may be borrowed by one requestor at a time. No reservations for a specific date will be accepted. It is most efficient to order via the web site.

Source: U. S. Environmental Protection Agency, Region 1
Customer Service Center
One Congress Street, Suite 1100
Boston, MA 02214
World Wide Web URL:
http://yosemite.epa.gov/r1/videolen.nsf/

Your Yard and Clean Air: What Can You Do to Prevent Pollution

Information on how to prevent air pollution.

Availability:	One copy to schools, libraries, and homeschoolers world-wide.
Suggested Grade:	6-12
Order Number:	420F94002
Format:	Article

Source: U. S. Environmental Protection Agency, NSCEP
P. O. Box 42419
Cincinnati, OH 45242-2419
Phone: 1-800-490-9198
Fax: 1-301-604-3408
World Wide Web URL:
http://www.epa.gov/ncepihom/orderpub.html
Email Address: nscep@bps-lmit.com

Aeronautic Nation

Covers aspects of flight including great aviation disasters, early aviators and experimenters.

Availability: All requesters
Suggested Grade: 6-12
Order Number: not applicable
Format: Web Site
Special Notes: This URL will lead you to a subject page. Then click on the appropriate subject heading.
Source: ThinkQuest
World Wide Web URL:
http://www.thinkquest.org/pls/html/think.library

Aeronautics

An educator's guide full of activities for teaching about aeronautics.

Availability: All requesters
Suggested Grade: K-4
Order Number: not applicable
Format: Downloadable Teacher's Guide
Source: NASA Spacelink
World Wide Web URL:
http://www.nasa.gov/audience/foreducators/topnav/
materials/listbytype/Aeronautics.html

AeroNet

History, Parts of Airplanes, Aerodynamics, and Career Opportunities are featured.

Availability: All requesters
Suggested Grade: 6-12
Order Number: not applicable
Format: Web Site
Special Notes: This URL will lead you to a subject page. Then click on the appropriate subject heading.
Source: ThinkQuest
World Wide Web URL:
http://www.thinkquest.org/pls/html/think.library

Airplanes!

Activities and experiments that tell how planes work.

Availability: Classroom quantities to schools, libraries, and homeschoolers in the United States and Canada.
Suggested Grade: 3-7
Order Number: order by title
Format: Brochure
Special Notes: May also be downloaded from the web site.
Source: Aircraft Owners and Pilots Association
Membership Publications
421 Aviation Way
Frederick, MD 21701
Phone: 1-301-695-2154
Fax: 1-301-695-2309
World Wide Web URL:
http://www.aopa.org/path/materials.cfm

Airplanes

After briefly discussing the history of flight and the contributions of the Wright brothers, Ms. Jennings and a group of students visit an airplane assembly plant. They learn about the design and engineering departments, different systems of an airplane, and wing function and structure. The visit includes construction of business and private aircraft.

Availability: Schools, libraries, and homeschoolers in the United States who serve the hearing impaired.
Suggested Grade: 4-8
Order Number: 13101
Production Date: 1998
Format: DVD
Special Notes: Produced by Oakleaf Productions.
Terms: Sponsor pays all transportation costs. Return one week after receipt. Participation is limited to deaf or hard of hearing Americans, their parents, families, teachers, counselors, or others whose use would benefit a deaf or hard of hearing person. Only one person in the audience needs to be hearing impaired. You must register--which is free. These videos are all open-captioned--no special equipment is required for viewing.
Source: Described and Captioned Media Program
National Association of the Deaf
4211 Church Street Ext.
Roebuck, SC 29376
Phone: 1-800-237-6213
Fax: 1-800-538-5636
World Wide Web URL: http://www.dcmp.org

All About the Earth

Tells children what makes the third planet from the sun so special.

Availability: All requesters through interlibrary loan.
Suggested Grade: K-4
Order Number: 735.1 A44 1999 VIDEOC
Production Date: 1999
Format: VHS videotape
Terms: These videotapes are available through interlibrary loan only. Simply request the specific video by name and number at your local public library, university library, or company library. The librarian will submit your request using an ALA interlibrary loan form, and the videos will be mailed to your library for your use. Interlibrary loans are limited to two videos at a time. The address listed below is for the ALA loan form only--your librarian must submit requests to this address.
Source: U. S. Geological Survey Library
345 Middlefield Road, MS 955
Menlo Park, CA 94025

All About the Moon

Gives children a close-up look at the moon while answering key questions, including "Why does the moon appear different every night? What does the moon look like up close? What is it like to walk on the moon?"

Availability: All requesters through interlibrary loan.
Suggested Grade: K-4
Order Number: 736 A44 1999 VIDEOC
Production Date: 1999

 Indicates an Internet Resource--just enter the URL and instantly access the FREE teaching aid you need!
All materials listed in this 2010-2011 edition are BRAND NEW!

31

Format: VHS videotape

Terms: These videotapes are available through interlibrary loan only. Simply request the specific video by name and number at your local public library, university library, or company library. The librarian will submit your request using an ALA interlibrary loan form, and the videos will be mailed to your library for your use. Interlibrary loans are limited to two videos at a time. The address listed below is for the ALA loan form only--your librarian must submit requests to this address.

Source: U. S. Geological Survey Library
345 Middlefield Road, MS 955
Menlo Park, CA 94025

All About the Stars

Students will learn about the lifespan of stars and the various stages they pass through.

Availability: All requesters through interlibrary loan.
Suggested Grade: K-4
Order Number: 734.4 S7277 1999 VIDEOC
Production Date: 1999
Format: VHS videotape
Terms: These videotapes are available through interlibrary loan only. Simply request the specific video by name and number at your local public library, university library, or company library. The librarian will submit your request using an ALA interlibrary loan form, and the videos will be mailed to your library for your use. Interlibrary loans are limited to two videos at a time. The address listed below is for the ALA loan form only--your librarian must submit requests to this address.

Source: U. S. Geological Survey Library
345 Middlefield Road, MS 955
Menlo Park, CA 94025

Alphabet of Space, An

Uses a rhyming technique to introduce basic space vocabulary words. Combines National Aeronautical and Space Administration footage, still photographs, and animation. Compares different objects in space and conditions on Earth and in space. Introduces various means of space exploration. Names the nine planets of the solar system. Examines gravity's effect on Earth and space. Shows that planets, moons, and satellites travel in orbits.

Availability: Schools, libraries, and homeschoolers in the United States who serve the hearing impaired.
Suggested Grade: 4-8
Order Number: 2449
Format: DVD
Special Notes: Produced by Coronet/MTI Film & Video Corp.
Terms: Sponsor pays all transportation costs. Return one week after receipt. Participation is limited to deaf or hard of hearing Americans, their parents, families, teachers, counselors, or others whose use would benefit a deaf or hard of hearing person. Only one person in the audience needs to be hearing impaired. You must register--which is free. These videos are all open-captioned--no special equipment is required for viewing.

Source: Described and Captioned Media Program
National Association of the Deaf
4211 Church Street Ext.
Roebuck, SC 29376
Phone: 1-800-237-6213
Fax: 1-800-538-5636
World Wide Web URL: http://www.dcmp.org

Amazing Space: Explorations

Interactive lessons about space.

Availability: All requesters
Suggested Grade: All ages
Order Number: not applicable
Format: Web Site

Source: Space Telescope Science Institute
World Wide Web URL:
http://amazing-space.stsci.edu/resources/explorations/

Arty the Part Time Astronaut

Students will learn about our solar system through games, quizzes, and fun activities.

Availability: All requesters
Suggested Grade: K-6
Order Number: not applicable
Format: Web Site

Source: 3 Pounds Press
World Wide Web URL:
http://www.artyastro.com/artyastro.htm

Ask the Answer Worm!

"It's a dirty job but someone has to do it." And so, S. K. Worm answers students questions about soil.

Availability: All requesters
Suggested Grade: 2-6
Order Number: not applicable
Format: Web Site

Source: U. S. Department of Agriculture, Natural Resources
Conservation Service
World Wide Web URL:
http://www.nrcs.usda.gov/Feature/education/
squirm/skworm.html

Astronomy Picture of the Day

Each day a different image or photograph of our fascinating universe is featured, along with a brief explanation written by a professional astronomer.

Availability: All requesters
Suggested Grade: All ages
Order Number: not applicable
Format: Web Site

Source: Robert Nemiroff and Jerry Bonnell
World Wide Web URL:
http://antwrp.gsfc.nasa.gov/apod/astropix.html

Astro-Venture

An interactive multimedia site that asks students to search for and create a planet suitable for human habitation while they act as NASA employees.

Availability: All requesters
Suggested Grade: 5-8
Order Number: not applicable
Format: Web Site

Source: NASA Quest
World Wide Web URL:
http://quest.arc.nasa.gov/projects/astrobiology/
astroventure/avhome.html

Atmosphere Ecolinks
Provides links to classroom activities, web sites, lessons, and more on this subject.
Availability: All requesters
Suggested Grade: 4-12
Order Number: not applicable
Format: Web Site
Source: Miami Museum of Science/Science Learning
Network
World Wide Web URL: http://www.miamisci.org/ecolinks/

Auroras: Paintings in the Sky
Shows what auroras look like on Earth and explains how they are created.
Availability: All requesters
Suggested Grade: All ages
Order Number: not applicable
Format: Web Site
Source: Mish Denlinger
World Wide Web URL:
http://www.exploratorium.edu/learning_studio/auroras/

Avalanche!
A team of scientists triggers an avalanche onto themselves in order to study its power and effects.
Availability: All requesters through interlibrary loan.
Suggested Grade: 4-12
Order Number: 245 A9242 1997 VIDEOC
Production Date: 1997
Format: VHS videotape
Terms: These videotapes are available through interlibrary loan only. Simply request the specific video by name and number at your local public library, university library, or company library. The librarian will submit your request using an ALA interlibrary loan form, and the videos will be mailed to your library for your use. Interlibrary loans are limited to two videos at a time. The address listed below is for the ALA loan form only--your librarian must submit requests to this address.
Source: U. S. Geological Survey Library
345 Middlefield Road, MS 955
Menlo Park, CA 94025

Aviation Through the Ages
Journey with Leonardo da Vinci for a look at the history of aviation.
Availability: All requesters
Suggested Grade: All ages
Order Number: not applicable
Format: Web Site

Special Notes: This URL will lead you to a subject page. Then click on the appropriate subject heading.
Source: ThinkQuest
World Wide Web URL:
http://www.thinkquest.org/pls/html/think.library

Biomes
Offers general information and descriptions of nine of the most common terrestrial biomes, five of the main marine biomes, and two of the standing water biomes.
Availability: All requesters through interlibrary loan.
Suggested Grade: 6-12
Order Number: 919 B5653 1998 VIDEOC
Production Date: 1998
Format: VHS videotape
Terms: These videotapes are available through interlibrary loan only. Simply request the specific video by name and number at your local public library, university library, or company library. The librarian will submit your request using an ALA interlibrary loan form, and the videos will be mailed to your library for your use. Interlibrary loans are limited to two videos at a time. The address listed below is for the ALA loan form only--your librarian must submit requests to this address.
Source: U. S. Geological Survey Library
345 Middlefield Road, MS 955
Menlo Park, CA 94025

Blast Off Into Space
Learn how to view the sky through binoculars, telescopes, or at an observatory. Learn about the various phenomena out in our solar system as well.
Availability: All requesters
Suggested Grade: 6-12
Order Number: not applicable
Format: Web Site
Special Notes: This URL will lead you to a subject page. Then click on the appropriate subject heading.
Source: ThinkQuest
World Wide Web URL:
http://www.thinkquest.org/pls/html/think.library

Born of Dreams, Inspired by Freedom
Commemorates the historic flight of the Wright Brothers.
Availability: All requesters
Suggested Grade: 6-12
Order Number: not applicable
Format: Web Site
Source: U. S. Centennial of Flight Commission
World Wide Web URL: http://www.centennialofflight.gov/

Bugwood Network, The
Provides information on forests--the pests that infect them, the management of them, and much more.
Availability: All requesters
Suggested Grade: 6-12
Order Number: not applicable
Format: Web Site

 Indicates an Internet Resource--just enter the URL and instantly access the FREE teaching aid you need!
*All materials listed in this 2010-2011 edition are **BRAND NEW!***

33

EARTH AND SPACE SCIENCE

Source: Warnell School of Forest Resources
World Wide Web URL: http://www.bugwood.org/

Build-a-Prairie
Choose the best plants and animals to bring to your prairie restoration site and be sure to avoid dangerous exotic species! Then watch the prairie come to life.

Availability: All requesters
Suggested Grade: All ages
Order Number: not applicable
Format: Online Game
Source: Minnesota IDEALS
World Wide Web URL:
http://www.bellmuseum.org/distancelearning/prairie/build/

Carbon Sequestration in Soils
Defines carbon sequestration and addresses benefits and potential costs of management techniques, the role of forests, and what scientists are doing to understand soil carbon sequestration.

Availability: All requesters
Suggested Grade: 6-Adult
Order Number: not applicable
Format: Online Fact Sheet
Source: Ecological Society of America, The
World Wide Web URL:
http://www.esa.org/education_diversity/factsheets.php

Carolina Coastal Science
A study of coastal life and the challenges we face in maintaining the ecological balance of these areas.

Availability: All requesters
Suggested Grade: 6-12
Order Number: not applicable
Format: Web Site
Source: Alec M. Bodzin
World Wide Web URL: http://www.ncsu.edu/coast/

Cavitation--A Bursting Bubble
This program explains the problems of cavitation caused by fast moving, confined water which can cause extensive and expensive repairs.

Availability: Schools, libraries, homeschoolers, nursing homes, and others in the United States and Canada.
Suggested Grade: 6-12
Order Number: order by title
Production Date: 1984
Format: VHS videotape
Special Notes: May be copied for permanent retention. Cleared for TV broadcast with advance permission.
Terms: Borrowers pay return postage. Return 30 days after scheduled showing, via U.S. Mail. Book 30 days in advance. Up to 2 videos will be sent out to one customer at a time. Your next order will be mailed as soon as you return previously borrowed tapes.

Source: Bureau of Reclamation
U.S. Department of the Interior
Attn: Kristi Thompson, Library, 84-21320
6th Avenue & Kipling Street, Building 67
Denver, CO 80225-0007
Phone: 1-303-445-2039
Fax: 1-303-445-6303
World Wide Web URL: http://www.usbr.gov/library
Email Address: library@do.usbr.gov

Changing Faces: A Study of Solar and Planetary Rotation Rates
Students will work as NASA scientists to make repeated observations of our Sun and the planets to determine their rotation rates.

Availability: All requesters
Suggested Grade: 5-8
Order Number: not applicable
Format: Online Teacher's Guide
Source: NASA/MSU-Bozeman CERES Project
World Wide Web URL:
http://btc.montana.edu/ceres/html/Faces/faces1.html

Chasing El Nino
Originally produced as an episode of the television program Nova, this video explores El Nino's myths, reveals its devastation and explains it's fascinating origins.

Availability: All requesters through interlibrary loan.
Suggested Grade: 6-12
Order Number: 510 C4274 1998 VIDEOC
Production Date: 1998
Format: VHS videotape
Terms: These videotapes are available through interlibrary loan only. Simply request the specific video by name and number at your local public library, university library, or company library. The librarian will submit your request using an ALA interlibrary loan form, and the videos will be mailed to your library for your use. Interlibrary loans are limited to two videos at a time. The address listed below is for the ALA loan form only--your librarian must submit requests to this address.
Source: U. S. Geological Survey Library
345 Middlefield Road, MS 955
Menlo Park, CA 94025

Classifying Galaxies
An interactive lesson on the Hubble System of classifying galaxies.

Availability: All requesters
Suggested Grade: 5-9
Order Number: not applicable
Format: Online Lesson Plan
Source: George and Jane Hastings
World Wide Web URL:
http://cse.ssl.berkeley.edu/segwayEd/lessons/classifying_galaxies/galaxy.htm

Cloud Quest
Learn about the clouds.

Availability:	All requesters
Suggested Grade:	3-6
Order Number:	not applicable
Format:	WebQuest

Source: Rebecca Keene, Robyn Greenstone, Shari Robinson, and Patty Sheeran
World Wide Web URL:
http://www2.lhric.org/kat/wq3rd.htm

COAST
Many resources for studying about oceans.

Availability:	All requesters
Suggested Grade:	4-12
Order Number:	not applicable
Format:	Web Site

Source: Consortium for Oceanographic Activities for Students and Teachers
World Wide Web URL: http://www.coast-nopp.org/

Collection of Connect-the-Dot Puzzles, A
Connecting the dots will show you historical aircraft from the Wright Flyer to the Space Shuttle.

Availability:	Classroom quantities to schools, libraries, and homeschoolers in the United States and Canada.
Suggested Grade:	K-4
Order Number:	order by title
Format:	Activity Sheet
Special Notes:	May also be downloaded from the web site.

Source: Aircraft Owners and Pilots Association
Membership Publications
421 Aviation Way
Frederick, MD 21701
Phone: 1-301-695-2154
Fax: 1-301-695-2309
World Wide Web URL:
http://www.aopa.org/path/materials.cfm

Comets
Discover what elements make up comets and learn more about Halley's Comet.

Availability:	All requesters
Suggested Grade:	3-6
Order Number:	not applicable
Format:	WebQuest

Source: Carolyn Starmer
World Wide Web URL:
http://can-do.com/uci/lessons98/Comets.html

Constellations, The
Here you will find all kinds of information relating to the 88 constellations.

Availability:	All requesters
Suggested Grade:	All ages
Order Number:	not applicable
Format:	Web Site

Source: Richard Dibon-Smith
World Wide Web URL:
http://www.dibonsmith.com/stars.htm

Coral Reefs
Addresses what coral reefs are, their ecological role, and major threats to their sustainability.

Availability:	All requesters
Suggested Grade:	6-Adult
Order Number:	not applicable
Format:	Online Fact Sheet

Source: Ecological Society of America, The
World Wide Web URL:
http://www.esa.org/education_diversity/factsheets.php

Decade of Destruction: Saga of the American Rainforest
Classroom version of a series originally aired on PBS.

Availability:	Schools, libraries, homeschoolers, and nursing homes in Illinois, Indiana, Iowa, Michigan, Minnesota, Missouri, Ohio, and Wisconsin only.
Suggested Grade:	7-12
Order Number:	303
Format:	VHS videotape
Terms:	Return postage is paid by borrower. Book 10-14 days in advance. Return 7 days after showing. Please provide alternate showing date.

Source: U. S. Fish and Wildlife Service
Region 3, Resource Library
3815 American Boulevard
Bloomington, MN 55425
Fax: 1-612-725-3279
Email Address: judy_geck@fws.gov

Dig--The Archaeology Magazine for Kids!
Supplement to Dig Magazine, this website introduces students to archaeology, paleontology, and earth sciences. Site includes teacher's guides.

Availability:	All requesters
Suggested Grade:	2-7
Order Number:	not applicable
Format:	Web Site

Source: Cobblestone Publishing Company
World Wide Web URL: http://digonsite.com/

Earth, A Young Planet?, The
Some say, "Earth is billions of years old." But, how has that been determined, and how accurate are the dates? Scientists discuss the various age estimation methods, how they work and reveal facts generally not discussed in public. There are alternate scientific age estimation methods that produce considerably lower ages. Hosted by A.E. Wilder-Smith.

Availability:	Public schools in the Continental United States. Others must pay a rental fee.
Suggested Grade:	5-Adult
Order Number:	order by title

Production Date: 1983
Format: DVD
Special Notes: Part of the Origins: How the World Came to Be Series.
Terms: Borrower pays return postage. Provide alternate showing date. Return 30 days after scheduled showing date via U. S. Mail. The video must be ordered by a teacher, principal, or school administrator on school stationery.

Source: Eden Communications
P. O. Box 200
Gilbert, AZ 85299
Phone: 1-800-332-2261
Fax: 1-480-507-3623
World Wide Web URL: http://www.eden.org/schools
Email Address: orders@eden.org

Earthquakes
Explains the nature and causes of earthquakes.
Availability: All requesters
Suggested Grade: 4-12
Order Number: not applicable
Format: Online Booklet; 20 pages
Source: USGS Information Services
World Wide Web URL: http://pubs.usgs.gov/gip/earthq1/

Endeavour Views the Earth Electronic Picture Book
An electronic picture book.
Availability: All requesters
Suggested Grade: All ages
Platform: Macintosh; Windows
Order Number: not applicable
Format: Downloadable Electronic Book
Special Notes: Macintosh requires HyperCard Player 2.1; Windows requires WinPlus Runtime.
Source: Exploration in Education
World Wide Web URL: http://www.stsci.edu/exined/

Eruption of Kilauea 1959-60
Illustrates the process leading to a volcanic eruption.
Availability: All requesters through interlibrary loan.
Suggested Grade: 7-Adult
Order Number: 220 (950) E786 1961 VIDEOC
Production Date: 1961
Format: VHS videotape
Terms: These videotapes are available through interlibrary loan only. Simply request the specific video by name and number at your local public library, university library, or company library. The librarian will submit your request using an ALA interlibrary loan form, and the videos will be mailed to your library for your use. Interlibrary loans are limited to two videos at a time. The address listed below is for the ALA loan form only--your librarian must submit requests to this address.
Source: U. S. Geological Survey Library
345 Middlefield Road, MS 955
Menlo Park, CA 94025

ExploreWorldOcean.com
Information and activities for all ages about the ocean.
Availability: All requesters
Suggested Grade: All ages
Order Number: not applicable
Format: Web Site
Source: Sean Chamberlin
World Wide Web URL: http://www.oceansonline.com/

Exploring Caves
Covers geology, cartography, and hydrology in a lighthearted story about Bat, who finds two lost children in a cave and teaches them various lessons as he guides them to safety.
Availability: All requesters
Suggested Grade: K-3
Order Number: not applicable
Format: Online Teaching Packet
Source: USGS Information Services
World Wide Web URL: http://egsc.usgs.gov/isb/pubs/teachers-packets/exploringcaves/

Exploring Meteorite Mysteries
This teacher's guide includes activities for earth and space sciences.
Availability: All requesters
Suggested Grade: 5-12
Order Number: not applicable
Format: Downloadable Teacher's Guide
Source: NASA Spacelink
World Wide Web URL:
http://curator.jsc.nasa.gov/outreach/expmetmys/index.cfm

Exploring Our Watershed System
Students will develop a knowledge and understanding of how watershed systems are made up.
Availability: All requesters
Suggested Grade: 9-12
Order Number: not applicable
Format: Online Lesson Plan
Source: Robert C. Suehr
World Wide Web URL:
http://sftrc.cas.psu.edu/LessonPlans/EarthSciences/Exploring.html

Exploring Planets in the Classroom
More than 25 hands-on science activities in classroom-ready pages for both teachers and students exploring Earth, the planets, geology, and space sciences.
Availability: All requesters
Suggested Grade: Teacher Reference
Order Number: not applicable
Format: Web Site
Source: Hawaii Space Grant Consortium
World Wide Web URL:
http://www.spacegrant.hawaii.edu/class_acts/index.html

Exploring the Earth Using Seismology

Explains how analyzing seismic waves create by earthquakes allows scientists to explore the Earth's deep interior.

Availability: Limit of 5 copies to schools, libraries, and homeschoolers world-wide.
Suggested Grade: 5-Adult
Order Number: order by title
Format: Handout
Special Notes: Email requests only. This publication can also be downloaded from the web site.

Source: Incorporated Research Institutions for Seismology
1200 New York Avenue, N. W., Suite 800
Washington, DC 20005
World Wide Web URL: http://www.iris.edu
Email Address: EandOproduct@iris.edu

Exploring the Earth Using Seismology

The paths of some of the seismic waves created by earthquakes and the ground motion that they caused are shown in this poster.

Availability: Limit of 5 copies to schools, libraries, and homeschoolers world-wide.
Suggested Grade: 5-Adult
Languages: English; Spanish
Order Number: order by title
Format: Poster
Special Notes: Email requests only.

Source: Incorporated Research Institutions for Seismology
1200 New York Avenue, N. W., Suite 800
Washington, DC 20005
World Wide Web URL: http://www.iris.edu
Email Address: EandOproduct@iris.edu

Eyes on the Sky, Feet on the Ground

Provides a wealth of hands-on astronomy explorations.

Availability: All requesters
Suggested Grade: 2-6
Order Number: not applicable
Format: Online Book

Source: Smithsonian Institution
World Wide Web URL: http://hea-www.harvard.edu/ECT/the_book/index.html

Fabulous Wetlands

The "Science Guy" extols the values and wonders of wetlands. Very fun.

Availability: Schools, libraries, and homeschoolers in Connecticut, Maine, Massachusetts, New Hampshire, Rhode Island, and Vermont.
Suggested Grade: K-4
Order Number: VID 029
Production Date: 1989
Format: VHS videotape
Terms: Borrower pays return postage. Return within three weeks of receipt. If the tape you request is available, it will be mailed within 5 business days. If not, you will be notified that this video is already out on loan. No more than three titles may be borrowed by one requestor

at a time. No reservations for a specific date will be accepted. It is most efficient to order via the web site.

Source: U. S. Environmental Protection Agency, Region 1
Customer Service Center
One Congress Street, Suite 1100
Boston, MA 02214
World Wide Web URL:
http://yosemite.epa.gov/r1/videolen.nsf/

Fabulous Wetlands

The "Science Guy" extols the values and wonders of wetlands. Very fun.

Availability: Schools, libraries, homeschoolers, and nursing homes in Illinois, Indiana, Iowa, Michigan, Minnesota, Missouri, Ohio, and Wisconsin only.
Suggested Grade: K-4
Order Number: 175
Format: VHS videotape
Terms: Return postage is paid by borrower. Book 10-14 days in advance. Return 7 days after showing. Please provide alternate showing date.

Source: U. S. Fish and Wildlife Service
Region 3, Resource Library
3815 American Boulevard
Bloomington, MN 55425
Fax: 1-612-725-3279
Email Address: judy_geck@fws.gov

Fire Ecology

Defines and discusses the role of fire in maintaining ecosystem health.

Availability: All requesters
Suggested Grade: 6-Adult
Order Number: not applicable
Format: Online Fact Sheet

Source: Ecological Society of America, The
World Wide Web URL:
http://www.esa.org/education_diversity/factsheets.php

Fire Mountain

"Captured in rare and spectacular aerial photography and survivor's own words and pictures, witness the terrifying fury of the worst volcanic disaster in American history."

Availability: All requesters through interlibrary loan.
Suggested Grade: 4-12
Order Number: 220(284) F5735m 1997 VIDEOC
Production Date: 1997
Format: VHS videotape
Terms: These videotapes are available through interlibrary loan only. Simply request the specific video by name and number at your local public library, university library, or company library. The librarian will submit your request using an ALA interlibrary loan form, and the videos will be mailed to your library for your use. Interlibrary loans are limited to two videos at a time. The address listed below is for the ALA loan form only--your librarian must submit requests to this address.

 Indicates an Internet Resource--just enter the URL and instantly access the FREE teaching aid you need!
All materials listed in this 2010-2011 edition are BRAND NEW!

37

EARTH AND SPACE SCIENCE

Source: U. S. Geological Survey Library
345 Middlefield Road, MS 955
Menlo Park, CA 94025

Floods
Outlines the basics of floods, how they are measured, their benefits, flood control, and land management.

Availability: All requesters
Suggested Grade: 6-Adult
Order Number: not applicable
Format: Online Fact Sheet
Source: Ecological Society of America, The
World Wide Web URL:
http://www.esa.org/education_diversity/factsheets.php

Fossils, Rocks, and Time
Explains the basics of how fossils are used in establishing time sequence in geology.

Availability: All requesters
Suggested Grade: 4-12
Order Number: not applicable
Format: Online Booklet; 24 pages
Source: USGS Information Services
World Wide Web URL: http://pubs.usgs.gov/gip/fossils/

Friendly Flame
Discusses the ecological benefits of an unusual land management strategy--Fire.

Availability: Schools, libraries, homeschoolers, and nursing homes in Illinois, Indiana, Iowa, Michigan, Minnesota, Missouri, Ohio, and Wisconsin only.
Suggested Grade: 6-12
Order Number: 72
Format: VHS videotape
Terms: Return postage is paid by borrower. Book 10-14 days in advance. Return 7 days after showing. Please provide alternate showing date.
Source: U. S. Fish and Wildlife Service
Region 3, Resource Library
3815 American Boulevard
Bloomington, MN 55425
Fax: 1-612-725-3279
Email Address: judy_geck@fws.gov

Galileo Animation
Animation of Galileo's probing mission to Jupiter. Educational Brief included.

Availability: Schools, libraries, homeschoolers, and nursing homes in Illinois, Indiana, Iowa, Michigan, Minnesota, Missouri, Ohio, and Wisconsin only.
Suggested Grade: 6-12
Order Number: 204
Format: VHS videotape
Terms: Return postage is paid by borrower. Book 10-14 days in advance. Return 7 days after showing. Please provide alternate showing date.

Source: U. S. Fish and Wildlife Service
Region 3, Resource Library
3815 American Boulevard
Bloomington, MN 55425
Fax: 1-612-725-3279

Email Address: judy_geck@fws.gov

Gems of Hubble 3.0 Electronic Picture Book
An electronic picture book.

Availability: All requesters
Suggested Grade: All ages
Platform: Macintosh; Windows
Order Number: not applicable
Format: Downloadable Electronic Book
Special Notes: Macintosh requires HyperCard Player 2.1; Windows requires WinPlus Runtime.
Source: Exploration in Education
World Wide Web URL: http://www.stsci.edu/exined/

Geologic Time
Explains relative and radiometric time scales and how geologists measure the age of the Earth.

Availability: All requesters
Suggested Grade: 4-12
Order Number: not applicable
Format: Online Booklet; 20 pages
Source: USGS Information Services
World Wide Web URL: http://pubs.usgs.gov/gip/geotime/

Global Climate Change
Discusses how Earth's climate is changing and its effects and explains what science is doing about it.

Availability: All requesters
Suggested Grade: 6-Adult
Order Number: not applicable
Format: Online Fact Sheet
Source: Ecological Society of America, The
World Wide Web URL:
http://www.esa.org/education_diversity/factsheets.php

Global Warming Facts and Our Future
Explores global warming and how it affects our future on Earth.

Availability: All requesters
Suggested Grade: 6-12
Order Number: not applicable
Format: Web Site
Source: National Academy of Sciences
World Wide Web URL:
http://www.koshlandscience.org/exhibitgcc/index.jsp

Grasslands
This program illustrates the ecological interrelationships of the grasslands biome, showing the locations of the world's grasslands and explaining how they may have originated.

Availability: Schools, libraries, homeschoolers, and nursing homes in Illinois, Indiana, Iowa,

Michigan, Minnesota, Missouri, Ohio, and Wisconsin only.

Suggested Grade: 6-12
Order Number: 403
Format: VHS videotape
Terms: Return postage is paid by borrower. Book 10-14 days in advance. Return 7 days after showing. Please provide alternate showing date.

Source: U. S. Fish and Wildlife Service
Region 3, Resource Library
3815 American Boulevard
Bloomington, MN 55425
Fax: 1-612-725-3279
Email Address: judy_geck@fws.gov

Great Divide, The--A Study of Continental Drift
Find a history of the continental drift, the scientists involved in studying it, and an extensive section on earthquakes.

Availability: All requesters
Suggested Grade: 6-12
Order Number: not applicable
Format: Web Site
Special Notes: This URL will lead you to a subject page. Then click on the appropriate subject heading.

Source: ThinkQuest
World Wide Web URL:
http://www.thinkquest.org/pls/html/think.library

Greenspirit: Trees Are the Answer
A documentary by Dr. Patrick Moore based on facts and science that provides insight into how forests work and how they can play a powerful role in solving many current environmental problems.

Availability: Schools, libraries, and homeschoolers in the United States and Canada.
Suggested Grade: 7-12
Order Number: order by title
Format: VHS videotape
Terms: Borrower pays return postage. Return within 15 to 30 days after receipt via United States mail. Provide alternate showing date.

Source: The Forest Foundation
853 Lincoln Way, Suite 104
Auburn, CA 95603
Phone: 1-866-241-8733
Fax: 1-530-823-1850
World Wide Web URL: http://www.calforestfoundation.org

Hands-On, Minds-On Meteorology Main Page
A collection of multimedia instructional modules that introduce and explain fundamental concepts in meteorology.

Availability: All requesters
Suggested Grade: 6-12
Order Number: not applicable
Format: Web Site

Source: Department of Atmospheric Sciences
World Wide Web URL:
http://www.atmos.uiuc.edu/courses/atmos100/

Home for Pearl
Teaches children about wildlife habitat and heightens their awareness of what wildlife needs to survive. Young viewers also learn about the difference between wild and domestic animals, urban wildlife, predators, endangered species, and the effects of habitat loss.

Availability: Schools, libraries, homeschoolers, and nursing homes in Illinois, Indiana, Iowa, Michigan, Minnesota, Missouri, Ohio, and Wisconsin only.
Suggested Grade: 1-9
Order Number: 77
Format: VHS videotape
Terms: Return postage is paid by borrower. Book 10-14 days in advance. Return 7 days after showing. Please provide alternate showing date.

Source: U. S. Fish and Wildlife Service
Region 3, Resource Library
3815 American Boulevard
Bloomington, MN 55425
Fax: 1-612-725-3279
Email Address: judy_geck@fws.gov

How A Plane Flies
How does a plane fly? What keeps it airborne? Presents the principles of flight and explains lift, thrust, gravity, and drag, the four forces that keep a plane aloft. Illustrates the four moveable parts of the wing and tail and how they function. Briefly describes different airplane engines.

Availability: Schools, libraries, and homeschoolers in the United States who serve the hearing impaired.
Suggested Grade: 5-9
Order Number: 13083
Production Date: 1995
Format: DVD
Special Notes: Produced by Landmark Media.
Terms: Sponsor pays all transportation costs. Return one week after receipt. Participation is limited to deaf or hard of hearing Americans, their parents, families, teachers, counselors, or others whose use would benefit a deaf or hard of hearing person. Only one person in the audience needs to be hearing impaired. You must register--which is free. These videos are all open-captioned--no special equipment is required for viewing.

Source: Described and Captioned Media Program
National Association of the Deaf
4211 Church Street Ext.
Roebuck, SC 29376
Phone: 1-800-237-6213
Fax: 1-800-538-5636
World Wide Web URL: http://www.dcmp.org

How Does a Seismometer Work?
Clearly answers this question.

Availability: Limit of 5 copies to schools, libraries, and homeschoolers world-wide.
Suggested Grade: 5-Adult
Order Number: order by title
Format: Handout

 Indicates an Internet Resource--just enter the URL and instantly access the FREE teaching aid you need!
All materials listed in this 2010-2011 edition are BRAND NEW!

39

Special Notes: Email requests only. This publication can also be downloaded from the web site.

Source: Incorporated Research Institutions for Seismology
1200 New York Avenue, N. W., Suite 800
Washington, DC 20005
World Wide Web URL: http://www.iris.edu
Email Address: EandOproduct@iris.edu

How Often Do Earthquakes Occur?

Explains that earthquakes are always happening somewhere.

Availability:	Limit of 5 copies to schools, libraries, and homeschoolers world-wide.
Suggested Grade:	5-Adult
Order Number:	order by title
Format:	One page handout
Special Notes:	Email requests only. This publication can also be downloaded from the web site.

Source: Incorporated Research Institutions for Seismology
1200 New York Avenue, N. W., Suite 800
Washington, DC 20005
World Wide Web URL: http://www.iris.edu
Email Address: EandOproduct@iris.edu

How Old Is That Tree?

Students will be able to tell how old a tree is and understand the growth process.

Availability:	All requesters
Suggested Grade:	4
Order Number:	not applicable
Format:	Online Lesson Plan

Source: Kimberly McDowell
World Wide Web URL:
http://sftrc.cas.psu.edu/LessonPlans/Forestry/HowOld.html

Hubble's Amazing Rescue

The unlikely story of how the world's most beloved telescope was saved.

Availability:	All requesters
Suggested Grade:	7-Adult
Order Number:	not applicable
Production Date:	2009
Format:	Streaming Video

Source: NOVA
World Wide Web URL:
http://www.pbs.org/wgbh/nova/programs/index.html

Hurricane

Hurricanes are nature's engines of death and destruction, the costliest natural disaster on earth. Explains how and where hurricanes formed; uses live footage to show the forces of wind, weather, and storm surge, and the damage they can do. Compares current information with historical knowledge and notes how forecasting has greatly improved. Explores how meteorologists work to understand and predict these brutal storm.

Availability:	Schools, libraries, and homeschoolers in the United States who serve the hearing impaired.
Suggested Grade:	7-10

Order Number:	12835
Production Date:	1995
Format:	DVD
Special Notes:	Produced by Ambrose Video Publishing, Inc..
Terms:	Sponsor pays all transportation costs. Return one week after receipt. Participation is limited to deaf or hard of hearing Americans, their parents, families, teachers, counselors, or others whose use would benefit a deaf or hard of hearing person. Only one person in the audience needs to be hearing impaired. You must register--which is free. These videos are all open-captioned--no special equipment is required for viewing.

Source: Described and Captioned Media Program
National Association of the Deaf
4211 Church Street Ext.
Roebuck, SC 29376
Phone: 1-800-237-6213
Fax: 1-800-538-5636
World Wide Web URL: http://www.dcmp.org

Hurricane Hunters, The

Here is where you will find information gathered from pilots who have actually flown into hurricanes.

Availability:	All requesters
Suggested Grade:	6-12
Order Number:	not applicable
Format:	Web Site

Source: Major Val Salva
World Wide Web URL: http://www.hurricanehunters.com/

Identifying Watersheds w/ Topographic Maps

Students will learn how to identify watersheds through the use of a topographic map.

Availability:	All requesters
Suggested Grade:	6-8
Order Number:	not applicable
Format:	Online Lesson Plan

Source: George Ness
World Wide Web URL:
http://sftrc.cas.psu.edu/LessonPlans/EarthSciences/
IdentifyingWatersheds.html

Impact Catastrophe Electronic Picture Book, The

An electronic picture book.

Availability:	All requesters
Suggested Grade:	All ages
Platform:	Macintosh; Windows
Order Number:	not applicable
Format:	Downloadable Electronic Book
Special Notes:	Macintosh requires HyperCard Player 2.1; Windows requires WinPlus Runtime.

Source: Exploration in Education
World Wide Web URL: http://www.stsci.edu/exined/

Interactive History of Flight

Information about history of aviation from the year 1400.

Availability:	All requesters
Suggested Grade:	4-12

Order Number: not applicable
Format: Web Site
Special Notes: This URL will lead you to a subject page.
                  Then click on the appropriate subject heading.
Source: ThinkQuest
World Wide Web URL:
http://www.thinkquest.org/pls/html/think.library

Internet Glossary of Soil Science Terms
Defines the many terms relating to soil science.
Availability: All requesters
Suggested Grade: 6-Adult
Order Number: not applicable
Format: Online Glossary
Special Notes: Print copies are available for $5 each.
Source: Soil Science Society of America
World Wide Web URL: http://www.soils.org/sssagloss/

It's Found Underground: Groundwater, Our Buried Treasure
Study guide and video provides three classroom activities for elementary and middle school students in learning about: groundwater, how it acts in the ground, how human and natural processes may contaminate it, and how each of us can prevent pollution before it starts.
Availability: Schools, libraries, homeschoolers, and nursing homes in Illinois, Indiana, Iowa, Michigan, Minnesota, Missouri, Ohio, and Wisconsin only.
Suggested Grade: K-8
Order Number: 465
Format: VHS videotape
Terms: Return postage is paid by borrower. Book 10-14 days in advance. Return 7 days after showing. Please provide alternate showing date.
Source: U. S. Fish and Wildlife Service
Region 3, Resource Library
3815 American Boulevard
Bloomington, MN 55425
Fax: 1-612-725-3279
Email Address: judy_geck@fws.gov

Journey of the Blob
Short film that will stimulate young viewers to explore, wonder, imagine, and question our part in the water cycle.
Availability: Schools, libraries, homeschoolers, and nursing homes in Illinois, Indiana, Iowa, Michigan, Minnesota, Missouri, Ohio, and Wisconsin only.
Suggested Grade: K-4
Order Number: 87
Format: VHS videotape
Terms: Return postage is paid by borrower. Book 10-14 days in advance. Return 7 days after showing. Please provide alternate showing date.
Source: U. S. Fish and Wildlife Service
Region 3, Resource Library
3815 American Boulevard
Bloomington, MN 55425

Fax: 1-612-725-3279
Email Address: judy_geck@fws.gov

Journey Through the Galaxy
Information and resources for teaching and learning about the solar system.
Availability: All requesters
Suggested Grade: 6-12
Order Number: not applicable
Format: Web Site
Source: Stuart Robbins and David McDonald
World Wide Web URL:
http://home.cwru.edu/~sjr16/advanced/index.html

Kansas Foundation for Agriculture in the Classroom Resources
An assortment of lessons and activities for learning about agriculture.
Availability: All requesters
Suggested Grade: K-12
Order Number: not applicable
Format: Web Site
Source: Kansas Foundation for Agriculture in the Classroom
World Wide Web URL:
http://www.ksagclassroom.org/classroom/index.html

Life in Lost Creek
Shows three fresh water ecosystems: fast moving water, slow moving water, and standing water. Ecological concepts of habitat, adaptation, and ecological niche are explained as well as population, food chains, transference of energy and the interaction between organisms.
Availability: Schools, libraries, homeschoolers, and nursing homes in Illinois, Indiana, Iowa, Michigan, Minnesota, Missouri, Ohio, and Wisconsin only.
Suggested Grade: 9-12
Order Number: 97
Format: VHS videotape
Terms: Return postage is paid by borrower. Book 10-14 days in advance. Return 7 days after showing. Please provide alternate showing date.
Source: U. S. Fish and Wildlife Service
Region 3, Resource Library, 3815 American Boulevard
Bloomington, MN 55425
Fax: 1-612-725-3279
Email Address: judy_geck@fws.gov

Lightning
Lightning is a very familiar natural force, but scientists don't know how it begins, what causes it, or why a bolt takes a particular path. Lightning kills 1000 people annually, can be 30 miles long, but less than an inch thick. Time-lapse photography and recollections from people who have experienced it firsthand provide an intense look at this awesome force of nature.

 Indicates an Internet Resource--just enter the URL and instantly access the FREE teaching aid you need!
All materials listed in this 2010-2011 edition are BRAND NEW!

41

Availability: Schools, libraries, and homeschoolers in the United States who serve the hearing impaired.
Suggested Grade: 4-12
Order Number: 13132
Production Date: 1995
Format: DVD
Special Notes: Produced by Ambrose Video Publishing, Inc..
Terms: Sponsor pays all transportation costs. Return one week after receipt. Participation is limited to deaf or hard of hearing Americans, their parents, families, teachers, counselors, or others whose use would benefit a deaf or hard of hearing person. Only one person in the audience needs to be hearing impaired. You must register--which is free. These videos are all open-captioned--no special equipment is required for viewing.

Source: Described and Captioned Media Program
National Association of the Deaf
4211 Church Street Ext.
Roebuck, SC 29376
Phone: 1-800-237-6213
Fax: 1-800-538-5636
World Wide Web URL: http://www.dcmp.org

Living Watershed, A

Overview of what a watershed is, how important it is and what you can do to help improve the quality of water in your watershed. Based out of Puget Sound in Washington State, but the concepts can apply anywhere.

Availability: Schools, libraries, homeschoolers, and nursing homes in Illinois, Indiana, Iowa, Michigan, Minnesota, Missouri, Ohio, and Wisconsin only.
Suggested Grade: 7-12
Order Number: 69
Format: VHS videotape
Terms: Return postage is paid by borrower. Book 10-14 days in advance. Return 7 days after showing. Please provide alternate showing date.

Source: U. S. Fish and Wildlife Service
Region 3, Resource Library
3815 American Boulevard
Bloomington, MN 55425
Fax: 1-612-725-3279
Email Address: judy_geck@fws.gov

Lost in Space

With sections such as an "A to Z Space Encyclopedia," this site on astronomy will prevent you from being "lost in space."

Availability: All requesters
Suggested Grade: 4-12
Order Number: not applicable
Format: Web Site
Special Notes: This URL will lead you to a subject page. Then click on the appropriate subject heading.

Source: ThinkQuest
World Wide Web URL:
http://www.thinkquest.org/pls/html/think.library

Magellan Highlights of Venus Electronic Picture Book

An electronic picture book.

Availability: All requesters
Suggested Grade: All ages
Platform: Macintosh; Windows
Order Number: not applicable
Format: Downloadable Electronic Book
Special Notes: Macintosh requires HyperCard Player 2.1; Windows requires WinPlus Runtime.

Source: Exploration in Education
World Wide Web URL: http://www.stsci.edu/exined/

Marvel of Flight, The

From the first ideas of Leonardo da Vinci to the jet age and space travel.

Availability: All requesters
Suggested Grade: 4-12
Order Number: not applicable
Format: Web Site
Special Notes: This URL will lead you to a subject page. Then click on the appropriate subject heading.

Source: ThinkQuest
World Wide Web URL:
http://www.thinkquest.org/pls/html/think.library

Military Aircrafts

Aircraft used by the military.

Availability: All requesters
Suggested Grade: 4-12
Order Number: not applicable
Format: Web Site
Special Notes: This URL will lead you to a subject page. Then click on the appropriate subject heading.

Source: ThinkQuest
World Wide Web URL:
http://www.thinkquest.org/pls/html/think.library

Minerals by Name

Just click on the name of a mineral and you will learn more about that mineral.

Availability: All requesters
Suggested Grade: 7-Adult
Order Number: not applicable
Format: Web Site

Source: Amethyst Galleries, Inc.
World Wide Web URL:
http://mineral.galleries.com/minerals/byname.htm

Mi-Net

Lots of information for studying about marine life and the oceans.

Availability: All requesters
Suggested Grade: All ages
Order Number: not applicable
Format: Web Site

Source: Marine Institute, The
World Wide Web URL:
http://www.mi.mun.ca/mi-net/topics.htm

Miracle Resource, The

Approaches all aspects of forest education in a simple and elegant fashion. Handles topics as varied as photosynthesis, animal habitat, fires, insects and disease, and more.

Availability: Schools, libraries, and homeschoolers in the United States and Canada.
Suggested Grade: 5-12
Order Number: order by title
Format: VHS videotape
Terms: Borrower pays return postage. Return within 15 to 30 days after receipt via United States mail. Provide alternate showing date.

Source: The Forest Foundation
853 Lincoln Way, Suite 104
Auburn, CA 95603
Phone: 1-866-241-8733
Fax: 1-530-823-1850
World Wide Web URL: http://www.calforestfoundation.org

MSC Educational Publications

A number of publications on many aspects of climate and weather.

Availability: All requesters
Suggested Grade: 4-12
Order Number: not applicable
Format: Online Articles

Source: Meteorological Service of Canada
World Wide Web URL:
http://www.msc.ec.gc.ca/education/toc_e.cfm

NASA's Great Observatories Kit

Includes the Hubble Space Telescope, the Chandra X-Ray Observatory, and the Compton Gamma Ray Observatory.

Availability: All requesters
Suggested Grade: 5-12
Order Number: not applicable
Format: Downloadable Models

Source: NASA Spacelink
World Wide Web URL:
http://www.nasa.gov/audience/forstudents/postsecondary/
features/F_NASA_Great_Observatories_PS.html

Natural Gemstones

Describes mineral and organic gemstones.

Availability: All requesters
Suggested Grade: 4-12
Order Number: not applicable
Format: Online Booklet; 16 pages

Source: USGS Information Services
World Wide Web URL: http://pubs.usgs.gov/gip/gemstones/

Nature's Systems

Mr. Know-It-Owl presents Nature's System. Narrated by Leonard Nimoy, Margaret O'Brien, and William Shatner, this program examines the delicate balance of plants and animals within their environment. For primary school age students.

Availability: Schools, libraries, homeschoolers, and nursing homes in Illinois, Indiana, Iowa, Michigan, Minnesota, Missouri, Ohio, and Wisconsin only.
Suggested Grade: preK-4
Order Number: 120
Format: VHS videotape
Terms: Return postage is paid by borrower. Book 10-14 days in advance. Return 7 days after showing. Please provide alternate showing date.

Source: U. S. Fish and Wildlife Service
Region 3, Resource Library
3815 American Boulevard
Bloomington, MN 55425
Fax: 1-612-725-3279
Email Address: judy_geck@fws.gov

NeMO

Studies the dynamic interactions between submarine volcanic activity and seafloor hotsprings at an observatory, Axial seamount.

Availability: All requesters
Suggested Grade: 3-12
Order Number: not applicable
Format: Web Site

Source: Pacific Marine Environmental Laboratory
World Wide Web URL:
http://www.pmel.noaa.gov/vents/nemo/index.html

North American Skies

A monthly guide to astronomical phenomena occurring over North America.

Availability: All requesters
Suggested Grade: 6-12
Order Number: not applicable
Format: Web Site

Source: Larry Sessions
World Wide Web URL:
http://home.comcast.net/~sternmann/

Ocean Explorer

Learn lots of information from this site about the oceans that surround us.

Availability: All requesters
Suggested Grade: 6-12
Order Number: not applicable
Format: Web Site

Source: National Oceanic and Atmospheric Administration

World Wide Web URL: http://www.oceanexplorer.noaa.gov

Out of the Inferno

Examine the terrifying and often unpredictable variety of a volcano's moods, from vast, swirling mudflows to the ash-clouds that choked the life from ancient Pompeii.

Availability: All requesters through interlibrary loan.
Suggested Grade: 5-12
Order Number: 220 097 1998 VIDEOC

 Indicates an Internet Resource--just enter the URL and instantly access the FREE teaching aid you need!
All materials listed in this 2010-2011 edition are BRAND NEW!

43

Production Date: 1998
Format: VHS videotape
Terms: These videotapes are available through interlibrary loan only. Simply request the specific video by name and number at your local public library, university library, or company library. The librarian will submit your request using an ALA interlibrary loan form, and the videos will be mailed to your library for your use. Interlibrary loans are limited to two videos at a time. The address listed below is for the ALA loan form only--your librarian must submit requests to this address.

Source: U. S. Geological Survey Library
345 Middlefield Road, MS 955
Menlo Park, CA 94025

PATH to Aviation

A teaching guide with modules that connect math, science, and geography to aviation.

Availability: Single copies to schools, libraries, and homeschoolers in the United States and Canada.
Suggested Grade: 6-12
Order Number: order by title
Format: Booklet
Special Notes: Photocopying is encouraged. May also be downloaded from the web site.

Source: Aircraft Owners and Pilots Association
Membership Publications
421 Aviation Way
Frederick, MD 21701
Phone: 1-301-695-2154
Fax: 1-301-695-2309
World Wide Web URL:
http://www.aopa.org/path/materials.cfm

Planetary System Electronic Picture Book, The

An electronic picture book.

Availability: All requesters
Suggested Grade: All ages
Platform: Macintosh; Windows
Order Number: not applicable
Format: Downloadable Electronic Book
Special Notes: Macintosh requires HyperCard Player 2.1; Windows requires WinPlus Runtime.

Source: Exploration in Education
World Wide Web URL: http://www.stsci.edu/exined/

Planet Pals

Activities and projects for celebrating Earth Day.

Availability: All requesters
Suggested Grade: K-5
Order Number: not applicable
Format: Web Site

Source: Planet Pals
World Wide Web URL:
http://www.planetpals.com/earthday.html

PlanetQuest Electronic Picture Book

An electronic picture book.

Availability: All requesters
Suggested Grade: All ages
Platform: Macintosh; Windows
Order Number: not applicable
Format: Downloadable Electronic Book
Special Notes: Macintosh requires HyperCard Player 2.1; Windows requires WinPlus Runtime.

Source: Exploration in Education
World Wide Web URL: http://www.stsci.edu/exined/

Planets or Not, Here We Come!

Students will develop their research skills as they find information about a specific planet in our solar system.

Availability: All requesters
Suggested Grade: 3-4
Order Number: not applicable
Format: WebQuest

Source: Stephanie Sirvent
World Wide Web URL:
http://projects.edtech.sandi.net/king/planets

Pond Life-Food Web

Film that explores the microcosmic world of a pond.

Availability: Schools, libraries, homeschoolers, and nursing homes in Illinois, Indiana, Iowa, Michigan, Minnesota, Missouri, Ohio, and Wisconsin only.
Suggested Grade: 9-12
Order Number: 110
Production Date: 1986
Format: VHS videotape
Terms: Return postage is paid by borrower. Book 10-14 days in advance. Return 7 days after showing. Please provide alternate showing date.

Source: U. S. Fish and Wildlife Service
Region 3, Resource Library, 3815 American Boulevard
Bloomington, MN 55425
Fax: 1-612-725-3279
Email Address: judy_geck@fws.gov

Prairie Potholes Are for People

Segments include: What is a Wetland? Values and benefits of wetlands--The Wetland Controversy.

Availability: Schools, libraries, homeschoolers, and nursing homes in Illinois, Indiana, Iowa, Michigan, Minnesota, Missouri, Ohio, and Wisconsin only.
Suggested Grade: 5-12
Order Number: 246
Format: VHS videotape
Terms: Return postage is paid by borrower. Book 10-14 days in advance. Return 7 days after showing. Please provide alternate showing date.

Source: U. S. Fish and Wildlife Service
Region 3, Resource Library, 3815 American Boulevard
Bloomington, MN 55425
Fax: 1-612-725-3279
Email Address: judy_geck@fws.gov

Rainforests: Proving Their Worth

Shows how international marketing of renewable forest products may provide inhabitants with the means to protect their vanishing lands.

Availability: Schools and libraries in Iowa, Illinois, Michigan, Minnesota, and Wisconsin.
Suggested Grade: 6-12
Order Number: ENVRFR13VHS
Production Date: 1990
Format: VHS videotape
Terms: Borrower pays return postage. Return 8 days after showing. Book 2 weeks in advance. Order may also be picked up for those near the Center.

Source: Center for Latin American and Caribbean Studies
UW-Milwaukee
P. O. Box 413
Milwaukee, WI 53201
Phone: 1-414-229-5987
World Wide Web URL: http://www.uwm.edu/Dept/CLACS
Email Address: audvis@usm.edu

Rainforests: Proving Their Worth

Is a living rain forest of greater economic value than one that has been cut down for timber or pasture land? International marketing of foods, cosmetics, and crafts derived from tropical forests may provide native inhabitants with the means to protect their vanishing lands. This video chronicles this promising new movement, to save the fast disappearing rain forests--by marketing renewable forest products.

Availability: Schools, libraries, homeschoolers, and nursing homes in the United States.
Suggested Grade: 6-Adult
Order Number: order by title
Production Date: 1990
Format: VHS videotape
Terms: Borrower pays return postage. Return the day after scheduled showing, via UPS or Priority Mail, insured for $100.00. Book 4 weeks in advance and include an alternate date. Order should include name of person responsible for handling the video, and complete mailing address. Please mention this Guide when ordering. Tapes may not be duplicated, edited or exhibited for a fee.

Source: Church World Service
Film & Video Library
28606 Phillips Street, P. O. Box 968
Elkhart, IN 46515
Phone: 1-800-297-1516, ext. 338
Fax: 1-574-262-0966
World Wide Web URL: http://www.churchworldservice.org
Email Address: videos@churchworldservice.org

Rainforests: Proving Their Worth

Shows how international marketing of renewable forest products may provide inhabitants with the means to protect their vanishing lands.

Availability: Schools, libraries, and nursing homes in the United States.
Suggested Grade: 6-12
Order Number: GE9-video
Production Date: 1990
Format: VHS videotape
Terms: Borrowers must have a User's Agreement on file with this source--available by mail or via the Internet. Return postage is paid by borrower; return 12 days after showing. Book at least three weeks in advance. All borrowers are limited to a total of ten items per semester.

Source: Latin American Resource Center
Stone Center for Latin American Studies
Tulane University
100 Jones Hall
New Orleans, LA 70118
Phone: 1-504-862-3143
Fax: 1-504-865-6719
World Wide Web URL:
http://stonecenter.tulane.edu/LARCLLCatalogue.htm
Email Address: crcrts@tulane.edu

Rock Cycle

Examines the importance of the rock cycle as a natural process and a key factor in geologic change, this program identifies sedimentary, igneous, and metamorphic rock classification.

Availability: Schools, libraries, homeschoolers, and nursing homes in Illinois, Indiana, Iowa, Michigan, Minnesota, Missouri, Ohio, and Wisconsin only.
Suggested Grade: 9-12
Order Number: 398
Format: VHS videotape
Terms: Return postage is paid by borrower. Book 10-14 days in advance. Return 7 days after showing. Please provide alternate showing date.

Source: U. S. Fish and Wildlife Service
Region 3, Resource Library
3815 American Boulevard
Bloomington, MN 55425
Fax: 1-612-725-3279
Email Address: judy_geck@fws.gov

Rocks For Kids

Lots of information as well as additional links concerning rocks and minerals.

Availability: All requesters
Suggested Grade: 3-12
Order Number: not applicable
Format: Web Site

Source: GMB Services
World Wide Web URL: http://www.rocksforkids.com/

Rolling Stone Gathers No Moss, But a Fifth Grade Science Student Does, A

Students will categorize living things found in a microhabitat as well as learn how to use a compass.

 Indicates an Internet Resource--just enter the URL and instantly access the FREE teaching aid you need!
All materials listed in this 2010-2011 edition are **BRAND NEW!**

45

Availability: All requesters
Suggested Grade: 5-8
Order Number: not applicable
Format: Online Lesson Plan
Source: Dennis G. Hahn
World Wide Web URL:
http://sftrc.cas.psu.edu/LessonPlans/Forestry/
RollingStone.html

Seasons in the Desert
This habitat story is really a study in adaptations. Plants and animals that live in the desert have special adaptations to help them survive in this environment.
Availability: Schools, libraries, homeschoolers, and nursing homes in Illinois, Indiana, Iowa, Michigan, Minnesota, Missouri, Ohio, and Wisconsin only.
Suggested Grade: 7-12
Order Number: 500
Format: VHS videotape
Terms: Return postage is paid by borrower. Book 10-14 days in advance. Return 7 days after showing. Please provide alternate showing date.
Source: U. S. Fish and Wildlife Service
Region 3, Resource Library
3815 American Boulevard
Bloomington, MN 55425
Fax: 1-612-725-3279
Email Address: judy_geck@fws.gov

Seasons in the Swamp
By exploring the yearly cycle of an unforgettable swamp, known as "Barley Barber," this video demonstrates the importance of preserving this often forgotten part of our natural world.
Availability: Schools, libraries, homeschoolers, and nursing homes in Illinois, Indiana, Iowa, Michigan, Minnesota, Missouri, Ohio, and Wisconsin only.
Suggested Grade: 7-12
Order Number: 82
Format: VHS videotape
Terms: Return postage is paid by borrower. Book 10-14 days in advance. Return 7 days after showing. Please provide alternate showing date.
Source: U. S. Fish and Wildlife Service
Region 3, Resource Library
3815 American Boulevard
Bloomington, MN 55425
Fax: 1-612-725-3279
Email Address: judy_geck@fws.gov

SERCC Weather Quiz, The
Weather related questions, updated daily.
Availability: All requesters
Suggested Grade: 2-8
Order Number: not applicable
Format: Web Site

Source: Southeast Regional Climate Center
World Wide Web URL:
http://www.dnr.sc.gov/cgi-bin/sercc/wx-quiz.cgi

757 Glider Kit
Each glider challenge calls for students to develop abilities to identify and state a problem, design a solution, implement a solution, and evaluate that solution.
Availability: All requesters
Suggested Grade: 5-12
Order Number: not applicable
Format: Downloadable Model
Source: NASA Spacelink
World Wide Web URL:
http://www.nasa.gov/audience/foreducators/topnav/
materials/listbytype/757.Glider.Kit.html

Signs of Fall and Winter
Video animation explains the reason for the seasons, relating the earth's position to the sun in all four seasons.
Availability: Schools, libraries, homeschoolers, and nursing homes in Illinois, Indiana, Iowa, Michigan, Minnesota, Missouri, Ohio, and Wisconsin only.
Suggested Grade: 4-12
Order Number: order by title
Format: VHS videotape
Special Notes: Closed captioned.
Terms: Return postage is paid by borrower. Book 10-14 days in advance. Return 7 days after showing. Please provide alternate showing date.
Source: U. S. Fish and Wildlife Service
Region 3, Resource Library
3815 American Boulevard
Bloomington, MN 55425
Fax: 1-612-725-3279
Email Address: judy_geck@fws.gov

Signs of Spring and Summer
Video animation explains the reason for the seasons, relating the earth's position to the sun in all four seasons.
Availability: Schools, libraries, homeschoolers, and nursing homes in Illinois, Indiana, Iowa, Michigan, Minnesota, Missouri, Ohio, and Wisconsin only.
Suggested Grade: 4-12
Order Number: 498
Format: VHS videotape
Terms: Return postage is paid by borrower. Book 10-14 days in advance. Return 7 days after showing. Please provide alternate showing date.
Source: U. S. Fish and Wildlife Service
Region 3, Resource Library
3815 American Boulevard
Bloomington, MN 55425
Fax: 1-612-725-3279
Email Address: judy_geck@fws.gov

Soil 4 Ever

A children's video about soil.

Availability:	Schools, libraries, homeschoolers, and nursing homes in Illinois, Indiana, Iowa, Michigan, Minnesota, Missouri, Ohio, and Wisconsin only.
Suggested Grade:	K-4
Order Number:	113
Format:	VHS videotape
Terms:	Return postage is paid by borrower. Book 10-14 days in advance. Return 7 days after showing. Please provide alternate showing date.

Source: U. S. Fish and Wildlife Service
Region 3, Resource Library
3815 American Boulevard
Bloomington, MN 55425
Fax: 1-612-725-3279
Email Address: judy_geck@fws.gov

Soil Lesson Plans

A number of lesson plans for learning more about, and working with, soil.

Availability:	All requesters
Suggested Grade:	All ages
Order Number:	not applicable
Format:	Online Lesson Plans

Source: Natural Resources Conservation Service
World Wide Web URL:
http://soils.usda.gov/education/resources/k_12/lessons/

Soil: We Can't Grow Without It

Explains the importance of soil.

Availability:	Schools, libraries, homeschoolers, and nursing homes in Illinois, Indiana, Iowa, Michigan, Minnesota, Missouri, Ohio, and Wisconsin only.
Suggested Grade:	All ages
Order Number:	5
Format:	Set of 80 slides
Special Notes:	Sound provided on audiocassette.
Terms:	Return postage is paid by borrower. Book 10-14 days in advance. Return 7 days after showing. Please provide alternate showing date.

Source: U. S. Fish and Wildlife Service
Region 3, Resource Library
3815 American Boulevard
Bloomington, MN 55425
Fax: 1-612-725-3279
Email Address: judy_geck@fws.gov

Solar Eclipses for Beginners

A complete primer on solar eclipses.

Availability:	All requesters
Suggested Grade:	4-8
Order Number:	not applicable
Format:	Web Site

Source: Fred Espenak
World Wide Web URL:
http://www.MrEclipse.com/Special/SEprimer.html

Solar System Bowl

Learn all about the vast solar system.

Availability:	All requesters
Suggested Grade:	3-5
Order Number:	not applicable
Format:	Online Lesson Plan

Source: Jane Whaling
World Wide Web URL:
http://www.col-ed.org/cur/misc/misc29.txt

Solar System Puzzle Kit

An activity for earth and space science.

Availability:	All requesters
Suggested Grade:	5-12
Order Number:	not applicable
Format:	Downloadable Activity

Source: NASA Spacelink
World Wide Web URL:
http://www.nasa.gov/audience/foreducators/topnav/
materials/listbytype/Solar_System_Puzzle_Kit.html

Space Food and Nutrition

Science and math activities for learning about nutrition and the special nutritional needs in space.

Availability:	All requesters
Suggested Grade:	K-8
Order Number:	not applicable
Format:	Downloadable Teacher's Guide

Source: NASA Spacelink
World Wide Web URL:
http://www.nasa.gov/audience/foreducators/topnav/
materials/listbytype/
Space_Food_and_Nutrition_Educator_Guide.html

Space Place, The

Activities and puzzles galore to teach young students about space.

Availability:	All requesters
Suggested Grade:	2-6
Order Number:	not applicable
Format:	Web Site

Source: California Institute of Technology
World Wide Web URL:
http://spaceplace.jpl.nasa.gov/en/site_map.shtml

Space Science Curriculum Standards Quilt

Each lesson plan or activities covered here is laid out in the form of a quilt. Just click on that particular patchwork square and you will find lessons and activities on that space science topic.

Availability:	All requesters
Suggested Grade:	3-Adult
Order Number:	not applicable
Format:	Web Site

Source: NASA, Jet Propulsion Laboratory
World Wide Web URL: http://quilt.jpl.nasa.gov

 Indicates an Internet Resource--just enter the URL and instantly access the FREE teaching aid you need!
All materials listed in this 2010-2011 edition are BRAND NEW!

47

Space Shuttle Glider
Build a 1:300 centimeters scale model of the U. S. Space shuttle orbiter.

Availability: All requesters
Suggested Grade: 5-12
Order Number: not applicable
Format: Downloadable Model

Source: NASA Spacelink
World Wide Web URL:
http://www.nasa.gov/audience/foreducators/topnav/
materials/listbytype/Space.Shuttle.Glider.html

Space Weather Today
Activities and information to make learning about earth and space science fun.

Availability: All requesters
Suggested Grade: All ages
Order Number: not applicable
Format: Web Site

Source: Regents of the University of Michigan
World Wide Web URL:
http://www.windows.ucar.edu/spaceweather/index.html

StarChild
Lots of information about the solar system and the universe.

Availability: All requesters
Suggested Grade: 3-8
Order Number: not applicable
Format: Web Site

Source: Joyce Dejoie and Elizabeth Truelove
World Wide Web URL:
http://starchild.gsfc.nasa.gov/docs/StarChild/StarChild.html

StarMap
Generates a map of the night sky based on whichever database is used.

Availability: All requesters
Suggested Grade: 4-12
Order Number: not applicable
Format: Downloadable FULL Program

Source: Scott D. Mikkelson
World Wide Web URL:
http://webpages.charter.net/thegl/starmap.html

Story of Luray Caverns, Virginia, The
Outlines the geological formation of Luray Caverns from the beginning of the Shenandoah Valley 600 million years ago. Also includes the history of discovery at this U. S. Natural Landmark.

Availability: One copy to schools, libraries, and
                             homeschoolers in the United States and
                             Canada.
Suggested Grade: 4-12
Order Number: order by title
Format: Booklet
Terms: Borrower pays return postage. Return 14 days after
                             showing. Cleared for TV broadcast.

Source: Luray Caverns
P. O. Box 748
970 US Highway 211W
Luray, VA 22835
Phone: 1-540-743-6551
Fax: 1-540-743-6634
World Wide Web URL: http://www.luraycaverns.com
Email Address: staff@luraycaverns.com

Stream Ecology
Discusses the physical and biological features of streams.

Availability: One   copy   to   schools, libraries, and
                             homeschoolers world-wide. May be copied.
Suggested Grade: 7-12
Order Number: Vol. 52, No. 1
Production Date: 2005
Format: Article
Special Notes: May also be downloaded from the web site.

Source: Kansas School Naturalist, The
Department of Biology, Box 4050
Emporia State University
Emporia, KS 66801-5087
Phone: 1-620-341-5614
Fax: 1-620-341-5607
World Wide Web URL:
www.emporia.edu/ksn/http://www.emporia.edu/ksn/
Email Address: ksnaturl@emporia.edu

Suited for Spacewalking
Lots of activities for teaching about how spacesuits operate to keep spacewalkers healthy and safe.

Availability: All requesters
Suggested Grade: 5-12
Order Number: not applicable
Format: Downloadable Teacher's Guide

Source: NASA Spacelink
World Wide Web URL:
http://www.nasa.gov/audience/foreducators/topnav/
materials/listbytype/
Suited_for_Spacewalking_Educator_Guide.html

Tonight's Sky Chart
A portion of this web site is devoted to showing us how the sky will look this evening.

Availability: All requesters
Suggested Grade: 5-Adult
Order Number: not applicable
Format: Web Site

Source: Earth & Sky Radio Series
World Wide Web URL: http://www.earthsky.org/

Tornado
Tornadoes, the most violent weather phenomena on earth, can occur anywhere in the world. Most, however, happen in the United States in "tornado alley," the states of Texas, Oklahoma, and Kansas. Briefly relates the weather conditions necessary to produce tornadoes. Ride with storm chasers as they pursue these violent storms. Eyewitness

accounts, time-lapse photography, and film footage capture the destructive power of tornadoes.

Availability: Schools, libraries, and homeschoolers in the United States who serve the hearing impaired.
Suggested Grade: 4-12
Order Number: 12853
Production Date: 1995
Format: DVD
Special Notes: Produced by Ambrose Video Publishing, Inc..
Terms: Sponsor pays all transportation costs. Return one week after receipt. Participation is limited to deaf or hard of hearing Americans, their parents, families, teachers, counselors, or others whose use would benefit a deaf or hard of hearing person. Only one person in the audience needs to be hearing impaired. You must register--which is free. These videos are all open-captioned--no special equipment is required for viewing.

Source: Described and Captioned Media Program
National Association of the Deaf
4211 Church Street Ext.
Roebuck, SC 29376
Phone: 1-800-237-6213
Fax: 1-800-538-5636
World Wide Web URL: http://www.dcmp.org

To the Moon
Presents the story behind the Apollo space program, including the historic walk on the moon in 1969.

Availability: All requesters through interlibrary loan.
Suggested Grade: 4-12
Order Number: 739 T6 1999 VIDEOC
Production Date: 1999
Format: VHS videotape
Terms: These videotapes are available through interlibrary loan only. Simply request the specific video by name and number at your local public library, university library, or company library. The librarian will submit your request using an ALA interlibrary loan form, and the videos will be mailed to your library for your use. Interlibrary loans are limited to two videos at a time. The address listed below is for the ALA loan form only--your librarian must submit requests to this address.

Source: U. S. Geological Survey Library
345 Middlefield Road, MS 955
Menlo Park, CA 94025

Tramp in the Darien, A
Ecological, economic, and social conditions met while traveling by bus, boat, and foot through the Darien, a rainforest region near the Panama-Colombia border area.

Availability: Schools, libraries, and nursing homes in the United States.
Suggested Grade: 6-12
Order Number: GELA9-video
Production Date: 1989
Format: VHS videotape
Terms: Borrowers must have a User's Agreement on file with this source--available by mail or via the Internet. Return postage is paid by borrower; return 12 days after

showing. Book at least three weeks in advance. All borrowers are limited to a total of ten items per semester.

Source: Latin American Resource Center
Stone Center for Latin American Studies
Tulane University
100 Jones Hall
New Orleans, LA 70118
Phone: 1-504-862-3143
Fax: 1-504-865-6719
World Wide Web URL:
http://stonecenter.tulane.edu/LARCLLCatalogue.htm
Email Address: crcrts@tulane.edu

Tropical Rain Forest
Here's a look at the interrelationships between the rich variety of plant and animal life and the humid environment of the tropical rain forest.

Availability: Schools, libraries, homeschoolers, and nursing homes in Illinois, Indiana, Iowa, Michigan, Minnesota, Missouri, Ohio, and Wisconsin only.
Suggested Grade: 9-12
Order Number: 390
Format: VHS videotape
Terms: Return postage is paid by borrower. Book 10-14 days in advance. Return 7 days after showing. Please provide alternate showing date.

Source: U. S. Fish and Wildlife Service
Region 3, Resource Library
3815 American Boulevard
Bloomington, MN 55425
Fax: 1-612-725-3279
Email Address: judy_geck@fws.gov

Understanding Volcanic Hazards
An understanding into this monumental geologic hazard.

Availability: All requesters through interlibrary loan.
Suggested Grade: 4-Adult
Order Number: 220 U523 1955 VIDEOC
Production Date: 1995
Format: VHS videotape
Terms: These videotapes are available through interlibrary loan only. Simply request the specific video by name and number at your local public library, university library, or company library. The librarian will submit your request using an ALA interlibrary loan form, and the videos will be mailed to your library for your use. Interlibrary loans are limited to two videos at a time. The address listed below is for the ALA loan form only--your librarian must submit requests to this address.

Source: U. S. Geological Survey Library
345 Middlefield Road, MS 955
Menlo Park, CA 94025

Universe, The
NASA footage, computer graphics, and visual effects teach about the vastness of the universe. Discusses light-years, galaxies, nebulae, and the birth, death, and evolution of stars. Mentions neutron stars, black holes, the big bang

 Indicates an Internet Resource--just enter the URL and instantly access the FREE teaching aid you need!
All materials listed in this 2010-2011 edition are BRAND NEW!

49

theory, star light and color, and other mysteries. States there are still unanswered questions and challenges us to continue exploring our universe.

Availability: Schools, libraries, and homeschoolers in the United States who serve the hearing impaired.
Suggested Grade: 9-Adult
Order Number: 13029
Production Date: 1995
Format: DVD
Special Notes: Produced by United Learning, Inc.
Terms: Sponsor pays all transportation costs. Return one week after receipt. Participation is limited to deaf or hard of hearing Americans, their parents, families, teachers, counselors, or others whose use would benefit a deaf or hard of hearing person. Only one person in the audience needs to be hearing impaired. You must register--which is free. These videos are all open-captioned--no special equipment is required for viewing.

Source: Described and Captioned Media Program
National Association of the Deaf
4211 Church Street Ext.
Roebuck, SC 29376
Phone: 1-800-237-6213
Fax: 1-800-538-5636
World Wide Web URL: http://www.dcmp.org

Virtual Solar System, The
Learn all about the nine planets in our solar system.

Availability: All requesters
Suggested Grade: 6-12
Order Number: not applicable
Format: Web Site
Special Notes: This URL will lead you to a subject page. Then click on the appropriate subject heading.

Source: ThinkQuest
World Wide Web URL:
http://www.thinkquest.org/pls/html/think.library

Volcanoes
Presents a summary of the nature of the earth processes that create common types of volcanoes around the world, along with an introduction to the techniques of volcano monitoring research.

Availability: All requesters
Suggested Grade: 4-12
Order Number: not applicable
Format: Online Booklet; 45 pages

Source: USGS Information Services
World Wide Web URL: http://pubs.usgs.gov/gip/volc/

Volcano World
An assortment of articles, pictures, movies, games, and links relating to volcanoes.

Availability: All requesters
Suggested Grade: All ages
Order Number: not applicable
Format: Web Site

Source: North Dakota and Oregon Space Grant Consortia
World Wide Web URL: http://volcano.oregonstate.edu/

Water and Weather
A children's video about water and weather.

Availability: Schools, libraries, homeschoolers, and nursing homes in Illinois, Indiana, Iowa, Michigan, Minnesota, Missouri, Ohio, and Wisconsin only.
Suggested Grade: K-4
Order Number: 228
Format: VHS videotape
Terms: Return postage is paid by borrower. Book 10-14 days in advance. Return 7 days after showing. Please provide alternate showing date.

Source: U. S. Fish and Wildlife Service
Region 3, Resource Library
3815 American Boulevard
Bloomington, MN 55425
Fax: 1-612-725-3279
Email Address: judy_geck@fws.gov

Wealth in Wetlands
A cooperatively produced video includes interviews with five farmers who believe there is a place for wetlands on their farms. Included are: brief overviews of wetlands losses, restoration methods, sources of help in wetlands conservation and restoration in the U.S.

Availability: Schools, libraries, homeschoolers, and nursing homes in Illinois, Indiana, Iowa, Michigan, Minnesota, Missouri, Ohio, and Wisconsin only.
Suggested Grade: 9-12
Order Number: 162
Format: VHS videotape
Terms: Return postage is paid by borrower. Book 10-14 days in advance. Return 7 days after showing. Please provide alternate showing date.

Source: U. S. Fish and Wildlife Service
Region 3, Resource Library
3815 American Boulevard
Bloomington, MN 55425
Fax: 1-612-725-3279
Email Address: judy_geck@fws.gov

Wetland Ecosystems I--Habitats, Communities, and the Diversity of Life
Units include adaptations, life cycles, food webs, and more.

Availability: All requesters
Suggested Grade: 4-6
Order Number: not applicable
Format: Downloadable Teacher's Guide and Lessons.

Source: Ducks Unlimited
World Wide Web URL:
http://www.greenwing.org/dueducator/lesson_plans.html

Wetland Ecosystems II--Interactions and Ecosystems
Units include wetland types, energy pyramids, abiotic factors, and more.

Availability: All requesters
Suggested Grade: 7-8
Order Number: not applicable
Format: Downloadable Teacher's Guide
                  and Lessons.
Source: Ducks Unlimited
World Wide Web URL:
http://www.greenwing.org/dueducator/lesson_plans.html

Wetland Ecosystems III--Evolution, Diversity and the Sustainability of Ecosystems

Subject areas include environmental impact assessment, sociopolitical considerations in environmental solutions, biodiversity, and much more.

Availability: All requesters
Suggested Grade: 9-12
Order Number: not applicable
Format: Online Lesson Plan
Source: Ducks Unlimited
World Wide Web URL:
http://www.greenwing.org/dueducator/lesson_plans.html

Wetlands for the Future

Provides a basic overview of what a wetland is and why wetlands are important to waterfowl and wildlife.

Availability: Schools, libraries, homeschoolers, and nursing homes in Illinois, Indiana, Iowa, Michigan, Minnesota, Missouri, Ohio, and Wisconsin only.
Suggested Grade: 4-12
Order Number: 452
Format: VHS videotape
Terms: Return postage is paid by borrower. Book 10-14 days in advance. Return 7 days after showing. Please provide alternate showing date.
Source: U. S. Fish and Wildlife Service
Region 3, Resource Library
3815 American Boulevard
Bloomington, MN 55425
Fax: 1-612-725-3279
Email Address: judy_geck@fws.gov

Wetlands In Crisis

Discusses the importance of wetlands, how we are in crisis, and what might be done to help.

Availability: Schools, libraries, homeschoolers, and nursing homes in Illinois, Indiana, Iowa, Michigan, Minnesota, Missouri, Ohio, and Wisconsin only.
Suggested Grade: 6-12
Order Number: 422
Format: VHS videotape
Terms: Return postage is paid by borrower. Book 10-14 days in advance. Return 7 days after showing. Please provide alternate showing date.
Source: U. S. Fish and Wildlife Service
Region 3, Resource Library
3815 American Boulevard
Bloomington, MN 55425

Fax: 1-612-725-3279
Email Address: judy_geck@fws.gov

Wetlands Mitigation

Highlights four master planned community developments which were designed with the impact on wetlands as a consideration. Either existing or newly created wetlands were incorporated into the development plans.

Availability: Schools, libraries, homeschoolers, and nursing homes in Illinois, Indiana, Iowa, Michigan, Minnesota, Missouri, Ohio, and Wisconsin only.
Suggested Grade: 5-12
Order Number: 189
Format: VHS videotape
Terms: Return postage is paid by borrower. Book 10-14 days in advance. Return 7 days after showing. Please provide alternate showing date.
Source: U. S. Fish and Wildlife Service
Region 3, Resource Library
3815 American Boulevard
Bloomington, MN 55425
Fax: 1-612-725-3279:
Email Address: judy_geck@fws.gov

Wetlands We Need Them

This video contains great footage of many great animals in the wetlands, and also covers the importance of preserving the wetlands.

Availability: Schools, libraries, homeschoolers, and nursing homes in Illinois, Indiana, Iowa, Michigan, Minnesota, Missouri, Ohio, and Wisconsin only.
Suggested Grade: 6-12
Order Number: 255
Format: VHS videotape
Terms: Return postage is paid by borrower. Book 10-14 days in advance. Return 7 days after showing. Please provide alternate showing date.
Source: U. S. Fish and Wildlife Service
Region 3, Resource Library
3815 American Boulevard
Bloomington, MN 55425
Fax: 1-612-725-3279
Email Address: judy_geck@fws.gov

Where the Hot Stuff Is: Volcanoes of the Earth and Solar System

A recording of a webcast present on this topic.

Availability: All requesters
Suggested Grade: 9-12
Order Number: not applicable
Production Date: 2010
Format: Streaming Video
Source: Smithsonian National Air and Space Museum
World Wide Web URL:
http://www.nasm.si.edu/webcasts/archive.cfm

 Indicates an Internet Resource--just enter the URL and instantly access the FREE teaching aid you need!
All materials listed in this 2010-2011 edition are BRAND NEW!

51

EARTH AND SPACE SCIENCE

Why Is the Sky Dark at Night?
This question was presented by a famous astronomer in 1826--this web site attempts to answer this question.

Availability: All requesters
Suggested Grade: All ages
Order Number: not applicable
Format: Web Site

Source: Paul Lutus
World Wide Web URL: http://www.arachnoid.com/sky/

Your Weight on Other Worlds
Find out how much you weigh on other planets.

Availability: All requesters
Suggested Grade: All ages
Order Number: not applicable
Format: Web Site

Source: Ron Hipschman
World Wide Web URL:
http://www.exploratorium.edu/ronh/weight/

 Indicates an Internet Resource--just enter the URL and instantly access the FREE teaching aid you need!
*All materials listed in this 2010-2011 edition are **BRAND NEW!***

Adaptations Adventure!

In this lesson, students will explore different aspects of animal adaptation, including structural and behavioral adaptations, camouflage, migration, and hibernation. Each student must conduct research, make an illustration of the mystery animal and its environment.

Availability: All requesters
Suggested Grade: 3
Order Number: not applicable
Format: WebQuest
Source: Claire Higgins, Laura Mase, and Erin McCracken
World Wide Web URL:
http://oncampus.richmond.edu/academics/education/
projects/webquests/adaptations/

Alien from Earth

Do the remains of a tiny hobbit-like creature found on the island of Flores belong to a new human species?

Availability: All requesters
Suggested Grade: 7-Adult
Order Number: not applicable
Production Date: 2008
Format: Streaming Video
Source: NOVA
World Wide Web URL:
http://www.pbs.org/wgbh/nova/programs/index.html

Archeology Dig

This plan provides students with experience in analyzing artifacts and relics and constructing a hypothetical scenario describing a prehistoric culture.

Availability: All requesters
Suggested Grade: 5-7
Order Number: not applicable
Format: Online Lesson Plan
Source: Sharin Manes
World Wide Web URL:
http://www.col-ed.org/cur/sst/sst72.txt

Ask a Scientist

Through this service, you can email your question to volunteer scientists located throughout the world and receive an answer.

Availability: All requesters
Suggested Grade: All ages
Order Number: not applicable
Format: Web Site
Source: Newton BBS
World Wide Web URL:
http://www.newton.dep.anl.gov/AAS

Ask Dr. Universe

Not only will you find answers to many science questions that have already been asked, but you can ask Dr. Universe your own questions, too.

Availability: All requesters
Suggested Grade: All ages

Order Number: not applicable
Format: Web Site
Source: Washington State University
World Wide Web URL: http://www.wsu.edu/DrUniverse/

Bionik

Information about bionics.

Availability: All requesters
Suggested Grade: 6-12
Order Number: not applicable
Format: Web Site
Special Notes: This URL will lead you to a subject page. Then click on the appropriate subject heading.
Source: ThinkQuest
World Wide Web URL:
http://www.thinkquest.org/pls/html/think.library

Bleaching

Info and simple experiments to enlighten you about the mechanism of bleaches.

Availability: All requesters
Suggested Grade: 6-12
Order Number: not applicable
Format: Web Site
Special Notes: This URL will lead you to a subject page. Then click on the appropriate subject heading.
Source: ThinkQuest
World Wide Web URL:
http://www.thinkquest.org/pls/html/think.library

Boats

Simple explanations and experiments using soap and sponges help clarify why some objects float and some sink. Explains why boats usually don't sink, and shows many different boats.

Availability: Schools, libraries, and homeschoolers in the United States who serve the hearing impaired.
Suggested Grade: 2-6
Order Number: 12378
Production Date: 1994
Format: DVD
Terms: Sponsor pays all transportation costs. Return one week after receipt. Participation is limited to deaf or hard of hearing Americans, their parents, families, teachers, counselors, or others whose use would benefit a deaf or hard of hearing person. Only one person in the audience needs to be hearing impaired. You must register--which is free. These videos are all open-captioned--no special equipment is required for viewing.
Source: Described and Captioned Media Program
National Association of the Deaf
4211 Church Street Ext.
Roebuck, SC 29376
Phone: 1-800-237-6213
Fax: 1-800-538-5636
World Wide Web URL: http://www.dcmp.org

Bringing the Rain to Kapiti Plain

LeVar Burton plans an adventure filled day around the

Indicates an Internet Resource--just enter the URL and instantly access the FREE teaching aid you need!
All materials listed in this 2010-2011 edition are BRAND NEW!

53

weather in this episode from the PBS children's series "Reading Rainbow." The feature book, narrated by James Earl Jones, tells of a young African boy who brings rain to his dry and thirsty pastures.

Availability:	Schools, libraries, homeschoolers, and nursing homes in the United States.
Suggested Grade:	3-9
Order Number:	order by title
Production Date:	1986
Format:	VHS videotape
Terms:	Borrower pays return postage. Return the day after scheduled showing, via UPS or Priority Mail, insured for $100.00. Book 4 weeks in advance and include an alternate date. Order should include name of person responsible for handling the video, and complete mailing address. Please mention this Guide when ordering. Tapes may not be duplicated, edited or exhibited for a fee.

Source: Church World Service
Film & Video Library
28606 Phillips Street, P. O. Box 968
Elkhart, IN 46515
Phone: 1-800-297-1516, ext. 338
Fax: 1-574-262-0966
World Wide Web URL: http://www.churchworldservice.org
Email Address: videos@churchworldservice.org

Challenge at Glen Canyon

Heavy spring snow caused heavy runoff which, in turn, caused flooding along the Colorado River System. Consequently, unwanted cavitation occurred in the spillways at Glen Canyon Dam. This program describes the methods employed in repairing the spillways.

Availability:	Schools, libraries, homeschoolers, nursing homes, and others in the United States and Canada.
Suggested Grade:	6-12
Order Number:	order by title
Format:	VHS videotape
Special Notes:	May be copied for permanent retention. Cleared for TV broadcast with advance permission.
Terms:	Borrowers pay return postage. Return 30 days after scheduled showing, via U.S. Mail. Book 30 days in advance. Up to 2 videos will be sent out to one customer at a time. Your next order will be mailed as soon as you return previously borrowed tapes.

Source: Bureau of Reclamation
U.S. Department of the Interior
Attn: Kristi Thompson, Library, 84-21320
6th Avenue & Kipling Street, Building 67
Denver, CO 80225-0007
Phone: 1-303-445-2039
Fax: 1-303-445-6303
World Wide Web URL: http://www.usbr.gov/library
Email Address: library@do.usbr.gov

Checklist of Common Native Plants

Groups the park's most common plants into communities where they are typically found.

Availability:	Limit of 5 copies to schools, libraries, and homeschoolers world-wide.
Suggested Grade:	6-Adult
Order Number:	order by title
Production Date:	2005
Format:	Brochure

Source: Acadia National Park
Information
P. O. Box 177
Bar Harbor, ME 04609
Phone: 1-207-288-3338
Fax: 1-207-288-8813
World Wide Web URL: http://www.nps.gov/acad
Email Address: acadia_information@nps.gov

Chewing Gum

A fun look at the history of chewing gum and how it is made.

Availability:	Schools, libraries, and homeschoolers in the United States who serve the hearing impaired.
Suggested Grade:	preK-4
Order Number:	12404
Format:	DVD
Terms:	Sponsor pays all transportation costs. Return one week after receipt. Participation is limited to deaf or hard of hearing Americans, their parents, families, teachers, counselors, or others whose use would benefit a deaf or hard of hearing person. Only one person in the audience needs to be hearing impaired. You must register--which is free. These videos are all open-captioned--no special equipment is required for viewing.

Source: Described and Captioned Media Program
National Association of the Deaf
4211 Church Street Ext.
Roebuck, SC 29376
Phone: 1-800-237-6213
Fax: 1-800-538-5636
World Wide Web URL: http://www.dcmp.org

Children's Video Encyclopedia: Tell Me Why Series

An award winning, unique, video encyclopedia based on the book series by Arkady Leokum. "Tell Me Why" answers questions asked by children in an informative, easy to understand manner aided by outstanding visuals.

Availability:	Schools, libraries, homeschoolers, and nursing homes in Illinois, Indiana, Iowa, Michigan, Minnesota, Missouri, Ohio, and Wisconsin only.
Suggested Grade:	K-4
Order Number:	37-43, 228
Format:	VHS videotape
Terms:	Return postage is paid by borrower. Book 10-14 days in advance. Return 7 days after showing. Please provide alternate showing date.

Source: U. S. Fish and Wildlife Service
Region 3, Resource Library
3815 American Boulevard
Bloomington, MN 55425

Fax: 1-612-725-3279
Email Address: judy_geck@fws.gov

Classification of Viruses

Explains what a virus is as well as why and how they are classified.

Availability: One copy to schools, libraries, and homeschoolers world-wide. May be copied.
Suggested Grade: 5-Adult
Order Number: Vol. 53, No. 1
Production Date: 2006
Format: Booklet
Special Notes: May also be downloaded from the web site.
Source: Kansas School Naturalist, The
Department of Biology, Box 4050
Emporia State University
Emporia, KS 66801-5087
Phone: 1-620-341-5614
Fax: 1-620-341-5607
World Wide Web URL:
www.emporia.edu/ksn/http://www.emporia.edu/ksn/
Email Address: ksnaturl@emporia.edu

Curse of T. Rex

A documentary on the legal battle surrounding "Sue," a magnificent Tyrannosaurus Rex fossil, found in the South Dakota badlands.

Availability: All requesters through interlibrary loan.
Suggested Grade: 4-12
Order Number: 675 C8773 1997 VIDEOC
Production Date: 1997
Format: VHS videotape
Special Notes: Closed captioned for the hearing impaired.
Terms: These videotapes are available through interlibrary loan only. Simply request the specific video by name and number at your local public library, university library, or company library. The librarian will submit your request using an ALA interlibrary loan form, and the videos will be mailed to your library for your use. Interlibrary loans are limited to two videos at a time. The address listed below is for the ALA loan form only--your librarian must submit requests to this address.
Source: U. S. Geological Survey Library
345 Middlefield Road, MS 955
Menlo Park, CA 94025

Dinosaurs! Dinosaurs!

Explains how scientists learn about dinosaurs. Paleontologists use detective techniques to uncover fossils. They deduce how dinosaurs lived, what they ate, how they moved, and how they cared for their families. Visit a dig and learn how fossils are preserved for study. Watch a skeleton be reconstructed. Leslie Nielson hosts this live-action/animated presentation.

Availability: Schools, libraries, and homeschoolers in the United States who serve the hearing impaired.
Suggested Grade: 4-8
Order Number: 12988

Production Date: 1993
Format: DVD
Special Notes: Produced by Barr Media Group.
Terms: Sponsor pays all transportation costs. Return one week after receipt. Participation is limited to deaf or hard of hearing Americans, their parents, families, teachers, counselors, or others whose use would benefit a deaf or hard of hearing person. Only one person in the audience needs to be hearing impaired. You must register--which is free. These videos are all open-captioned--no special equipment is required for viewing.
Source: Described and Captioned Media Program
National Association of the Deaf
4211 Church Street Ext.
Roebuck, SC 29376
Phone: 1-800-237-6213
Fax: 1-800-538-5636
World Wide Web URL: http://www.dcmp.org

Dinosaurs: Facts and Fiction

Answers a series of basic questions on dinosaurs.

Availability: All requesters
Suggested Grade: 4-12
Order Number: not applicable
Format: Online Leaflet; 10 pages
Source: USGS Information Services
World Wide Web URL: http://pubs.usgs.gov/gip/dinosaurs/

Dinosaurs on Earth: Then...and Now

Do dinosaurs still live on earth? Begins with an animated look at the dinosaur eras. Paleontologists, recent fossil discoveries, and skeletal reconstructions reveal characteristics of different dinosaurs. Discover similarities between dinosaurs and today's animals by comparing their bones, shapes, and behaviors. Discusses T. Rex, Utahsaurus, brontosaurus, and others.

Availability: Schools, libraries, and homeschoolers in the United States who serve the hearing impaired.
Suggested Grade: 6-Adult
Order Number: 12989
Production Date: 1995
Format: DVD
Special Notes: Produced by National Geographic Society.
Terms: Sponsor pays all transportation costs. Return one week after receipt. Participation is limited to deaf or hard of hearing Americans, their parents, families, teachers, counselors, or others whose use would benefit a deaf or hard of hearing person. Only one person in the audience needs to be hearing impaired. You must register--which is free. These videos are all open-captioned--no special equipment is required for viewing.
Source: Described and Captioned Media Program
National Association of the Deaf
4211 Church Street Ext.
Roebuck, SC 29376
Phone: 1-800-237-6213
Fax: 1-800-538-5636
World Wide Web URL: http://www.dcmp.org

Indicates an Internet Resource--just enter the URL and instantly access the FREE teaching aid you need!
All materials listed in this 2010-2011 edition are BRAND NEW!

55

Electric Car, The: A Glimpse into the Future

Learn how to build your own, read about design, efficiency, problems, and possibilities.

Availability: All requesters
Suggested Grade: 9-12
Order Number: not applicable
Format: Web Site
Special Notes: This URL will lead you to a subject page. Then click on the appropriate subject heading.

Source: ThinkQuest
World Wide Web URL:
http://www.thinkquest.org/pls/html/think.library

Electronic Uses

Young students learn about the wonders of electronics.

Availability: All requesters
Suggested Grade: 6-8
Order Number: not applicable
Format: Web Site
Special Notes: This URL will lead you to a subject page. Then click on the appropriate subject heading.

Source: ThinkQuest
World Wide Web URL:
http://www.thinkquest.org/pls/html/think.library

Energy Behind Finding Energy, The

A two-part video that gives an overview of exploration, drilling and production of oil and natural gas.

Availability: Schools, libraries, and homeschoolers in OKLAHOMA only..
Suggested Grade: All ages
Order Number: order by title
Format: DVD
Special Notes: **May be retained permanently.**

Source: Oklahoma Energy Resources Board
Carla Zappola
3555 NW 58th, Suite 430
Oklahoma City, OK 73112
Phone: 1-405-942-5323
Fax: 1-405-942-3435
World Wide Web URL: http://www.oerb.com
Email Address: czappola@oerb.com

Farm to Fork Pasta Sample

A small bag showing separate sections of durum wheat, semolina and pasta with an information card.

Availability: Single copies to schools, libraries, and homeschoolers in the United States.
Suggested Grade: K-12
Order Number: order by title
Format: Sample of wheat

Source: North Dakota Wheat Commission
2401 46th Avenue SE, Suite 104
Mandan, ND 58554-4829
Phone: 1-701-328-5111
Fax: 1-701-663-5787
World Wide Web URL: http://www.ndwheat.com
Email Address: ndwheat@ndwheat.com

Funology.com--The Science of Having Fun

A bright website that will teach kids a lot about science while they have a great time.

Availability: All requesters
Suggested Grade: K-5
Order Number: not applicable
Format: Web Site

Source: Funburst Media, LLC
World Wide Web URL: http://www.funology.com/

Girlstart

Girlstart is a nonprofit organization that promotes, mathematics, science, and technology related skills for girls. This site provides games, activities, and information to this audience.

Availability: All requesters
Suggested Grade: 5-8
Order Number: not applicable
Format: Web Site

Source: Girlstart
World Wide Web URL: http://www.girlstart.org/

Great Dinosaur Mystery, The

Recent discoveries seem to indicate that man and dinosaurs once coexisted. This program includes an apparent "plesiosaur" carcass netted near New Zealand, plus numerous ancient drawings and legends of dinosaur-like creatures. Did dinosaurs actually become extinct millions of years before the existence of humans? Perhaps not!

Availability: Public schools in the Continental United States. Others must pay a rental fee.
Suggested Grade: 5-Adult
Order Number: order by title
Production Date: 1979
Format: DVD
Terms: Borrower pays return postage. Provide alternate showing date. Return 30 days after scheduled showing date via U. S. Mail. The video must be ordered by a teacher, principal, or school administrator on school stationery.

Source: Eden Communications
P. O. Box 200
Gilbert, AZ 85299
Phone: 1-800-332-2261
Fax: 1-480-507-3623
World Wide Web URL: http://www.eden.org/schools
Email Address: orders@eden.org

Growing Cane Sugar Crystals on a Small Scale

Two methods of growing crystals of "sucrose" in the classroom are detailed in this kit.

Availability: One kit to schools and homeschoolers WEST OF THE MISSISSIPPI ONLY. May be copied. Send a self-addressed business-size envelope. Make request on official stationery.
Suggested Grade: 4-12
Order Number: order by title
Format: Teacher's Kit

Source: C & H Sugar Co., Inc.
Connie C. Hunter
Consumer Affairs Administrator
830 Loring Avenue
Crockett, CA 94525
Fax: 1-510-787-4245
Email Address: conniehunter@chsugar.com

Hard Rock Mining Poster
Shows how taconite is made to be use din steel.

Availability:	Available while supplies last to schools, libraries, and homeschoolers in the United States and Canada.
Suggested Grade:	4-6
Order Number:	order by title
Format:	Poster

Source: Iron Mining Association of Minnesota
324 West Superior Street, Suite 502
Duluth, MN 55802
World Wide Web URL:
www.taconite.orghttp://www.taconite.org

History of Iron Mining in the Great Lakes Region
Details the history of this great industry.

Availability:	Available while supplies last to schools, libraries, and homeschoolers in the United States and Canada.
Suggested Grade:	9-12
Order Number:	order by title
Format:	Booklet

Source: Iron Mining Association of Minnesota
324 West Superior Street, Suite 502
Duluth, MN 55802
World Wide Web URL:
www.taconite.orghttp://www.taconite.org

How Plants Are Used
Reviews the many products that plants provide: including wood, paper, cotton, as well as food and medicines; also reminds viewers that fossil fuels we use today are derived from ancient plants.

Availability:	Schools, libraries, homeschoolers, and nursing homes in Illinois, Indiana, Iowa, Michigan, Minnesota, Missouri, Ohio, and Wisconsin only.
Suggested Grade:	9-12
Order Number:	350
Format:	VHS videotape
Terms:	Return postage is paid by borrower. Book 10-14 days in advance. Return 7 days after showing. Please provide alternate showing date.

Source: U. S. Fish and Wildlife Service
Region 3, Resource Library
3815 American Boulevard
Bloomington, MN 55425
Fax: 1-612-725-3279
Email Address: judy_geck@fws.gov

Invasion
Presents information on the increase of invasions by nonnative species, the threats they impose, and what can be done.

Availability:	All requesters
Suggested Grade:	6-Adult
Order Number:	not applicable
Format:	Online Fact Sheet

Source: Ecological Society of America, The
World Wide Web URL:
http://www.esa.org/education_diversity/factsheets.php

Jefferson Lab--Science Education
Lesson plans, activities, worksheets, games, and more are found on this site to help teachers and students in the study of math and science.

Availability:	All requesters
Suggested Grade:	3-8
Order Number:	not applicable
Format:	Web Site

Source: Jefferson Office of Science Education
World Wide Web URL: http://education.jlab.org/index.html

Journey Into Science
Lots of information helpful for teaching science.

Availability:	All requesters
Suggested Grade:	All ages
Order Number:	not applicable
Format:	Web Site

Source: Larry Jones
World Wide Web URL:
http://www.sciencebyjones.com/index.htm

Kid's Domain - Earth Day
Games, downloads, cards, songs, activities, and much more for celebrating Earth day.

Availability:	All requesters
Suggested Grade:	K-5
Order Number:	not applicable
Format:	Web Site

Source: Kid's Domain, The
World Wide Web URL:
http://www.kidsdomain.com/holiday/earthday/

Lasers in Everyday Life
Applications for the lasers that affect us all.

Availability:	All requesters
Suggested Grade:	All ages
Order Number:	not applicable
Format:	Web Site
Special Notes:	This URL will lead you to a subject page. Then click on the appropriate subject heading.

Source: ThinkQuest
World Wide Web URL:
http://www.thinkquest.org/pls/html/think.library

Light
Explains how all of the colors of the spectrum are made up

 Indicates an Internet Resource--just enter the URL and instantly access the FREE teaching aid you need!
All materials listed in this 2010-2011 edition are BRAND NEW!

57

of different lights.

Availability: All requesters
Suggested Grade: 6-12
Order Number: not applicable
Format: Online Lesson Plan
Source: Consuela Llamas
World Wide Web URL:
http://teachertech.rice.edu/Participants/cllamas/
lessons/science/light/studentlight.htm

Light & Color

An elementary class prepares for a visit from the Shadow Players, a group who use light, shadow, and color to tell a story. The class learns about sources of light, shadows, and silhouettes. They experiment with transparent, opaque, and translucent objects to see what lets light through. Using a prism, they discover the colors in light. Review at the end.

Availability: Schools, libraries, and homeschoolers in the United States who serve the hearing impaired.
Suggested Grade: 2-5
Order Number: 13010
Production Date: 1993
Format: DVD
Special Notes: Produced by ACG/United Learning.
Terms: Sponsor pays all transportation costs. Return one week after receipt. Participation is limited to deaf or hard of hearing Americans, their parents, families, teachers, counselors, or others whose use would benefit a deaf or hard of hearing person. Only one person in the audience needs to be hearing impaired. You must register--which is free. These videos are all open-captioned--no special equipment is required for viewing.
Source: Described and Captioned Media Program
National Association of the Deaf
4211 Church Street Ext.
Roebuck, SC 29376
Phone: 1-800-237-6213
Fax: 1-800-538-5636
World Wide Web URL: http://www.dcmp.org

Magic Mirror Box

Provides students with a hands-on activity which will stimulate their interest in observing, inquiring, and experimenting.

Availability: All requesters
Suggested Grade: 4-12
Order Number: not applicable
Format: Online Lesson Plan
Source: Patricia Brickley
World Wide Web URL:
http://www.col-ed.org/cur/sci/sci169.txt

Maple Syrup Lesson Plan

Students will learn to identify a sugar maple and explain how maple syrup is produced.

Availability: All requesters
Suggested Grade: K
Order Number: not applicable

Format: Online Lesson Plan
Source: Marguerite Wills
World Wide Web URL:
http://sftrc.cas.psu.edu/LessonPlans/Forestry/
MapleSyrup.html

Megabeasts' Sudden Death

Scientists propose a radical new idea of what killed off mammoths and other large animals at the end of the Ice Age.

Availability: All requesters
Suggested Grade: 7-Adult
Order Number: not applicable
Production Date: 2009
Format: Streaming Video
Source: NOVA
World Wide Web URL:
http://www.pbs.org/wgbh/nova/programs/index.html

Metric Temperature

Provides examples of the Antoine frame-of-reference method of learning the metric system, as it relates to temperature.

Availability: All requesters.
Suggested Grade: 3-12
Order Number: not applicable
Format: Downloadable Article
Source: U. S. Metric Association, Inc.
World Wide Web URL: http://www.metric.org

Microscope, The: Our Window on the World

Gives a general introduction to microscopes.

Availability: Schools, libraries, and homeschoolers in the United States who serve the hearing impaired.
Suggested Grade: 4-8
Order Number: 13389
Format: DVD
Special Notes: Also available as live streaming video over the Internet.
Terms: Sponsor pays all transportation costs. Return one week after receipt. Participation is limited to deaf or hard of hearing Americans, their parents, families, teachers, counselors, or others whose use would benefit a deaf or hard of hearing person. Only one person in the audience needs to be hearing impaired. You must register--which is free. These videos are all open-captioned--no special equipment is required for viewing.
Source: Described and Captioned Media Program
National Association of the Deaf
4211 Church Street Ext.
Roebuck, SC 29376
Phone: 1-800-237-6213
Fax: 1-800-538-5636
World Wide Web URL: http://www.dcmp.org

MooMilk.com

Provides everything you probably want to know about milk and cows.

Availability: All requesters
Suggested Grade: All ages
Order Number: not applicable
Format: Web Site

Source: MooMilk.com
World Wide Web URL: http://www.moomilk.com

Mousetrap Racer!!!

Learn about and have fun with mousetrap cars.
Availability: All requesters
Suggested Grade: 6-12
Order Number: not applicable
Format: WebQuest
Source: Robert Valadez
World Wide Web URL:
http://www.can-do.com/uci/ssi2002/mousetrap-racer.html

Ms. Gould's Question of the Week

Here's a science question of the week--no answer is provided as that is up to the students!
Availability: All requesters
Suggested Grade: 7-8
Order Number: not applicable
Format: Web Site
Source: Ms. Gould
World Wide Web URL:
http://www.thinkscience.org/QotW.html

North American Drought: A Paleo Perspective

Documents drought conditions in North America as many as 10,000 years ago and explains climate processes underlying those conditions.
Availability: All requesters
Suggested Grade: 9-Adult
Order Number: not applicable
Format: Web Site
Source: National Oceanic and Atmospheric Administration
Paleoclimatology Program
World Wide Web URL:
http://www.ngdc.noaa.gov/paleo/drought/drght_home.html

Nova

Provides information to help explain current events in the field of science.
Availability: All requesters
Suggested Grade: 6-12
Order Number: not applicable
Format: Web Site
Source: Australian Academy of Science
World Wide Web URL: http://www.science.org.au/nova/

Official String Theory Web Site, The

"Everything you always wanted to know about string theory, now in one convenient location."
Availability: All requesters
Suggested Grade: All ages
Order Number: not applicable
Format: Web Site
Source: Patricia Schwarz
World Wide Web URL: http://www.superstringtheory.com/

Online Experiments

Here are experiments using common household items, using your computer, or using the Shockwave plug-in which is available free over the Internet.
Availability: All requesters
Suggested Grade: All ages
Order Number: not applicable
Format: Web Site
Source: Little Shop of Physics
World Wide Web URL:
http://littleshop.physics.colostate.edu/onlineexperiments.htm

Open Door Web Site, The

Information on virtually every science area can be found here.
Availability: All requesters
Suggested Grade: All ages
Order Number: not applicable
Format: Web Site
Source: Ecole Active Bilingue Jeannine Manuel
World Wide Web URL: http://www.knockonthedoor.com/

Owl TV (Programs 31-40)

Children from ages 7-13 will enjoy this innovative and involving nature, science, and environment series. A wide range of subjects including animals, science, experiments, bodies, the future, and the environment. These programs encourage scientific literacy and develop skills in language, comprehension, grouping, manipulating data, and problem solving. Recommend showing one episode per week.
Availability: Schools, libraries, homeschoolers, and nursing homes in Illinois, Indiana, Iowa, Michigan, Minnesota, Missouri, Ohio, and Wisconsin only.
Suggested Grade: K-5
Order Number: 289-298
Format: Set of 10 VHS videotapes
Terms: Return postage is paid by borrower. Book 10-14 days in advance. Return 7 days after showing. Please provide alternate showing date.
Source: U. S. Fish and Wildlife Service
Region 3, Resource Library
3815 American Boulevard
Bloomington, MN 55425
Fax: 1-612-725-3279
Email Address: judy_geck@fws.gov

Paper Plate Education

An assortment of hands-on activities that use paper plates to supplement lessons in a range of science topics.
Availability: All requesters
Suggested Grade: K-8
Order Number: not applicable
Format: Web Site

 Indicates an Internet Resource--just enter the URL and instantly access the FREE teaching aid you need!
All materials listed in this 2010-2011 edition are BRAND NEW!

59

Source: Chuck Bueter
World Wide Web URL:
http://analyzer.depaul.edu/paperplate/

Preparing a Science Fair Project
Find out how to prepare and carry out a science project that will be fun and interesting.
Availability: All requesters
Suggested Grade: All ages
Order Number: not applicable
Format: WebQuest
Source: Gerald Robillard
World Wide Web URL:
http://www.qesn.meq.gouv.qc.ca/schools/olp/
webquest/sciwq.htm

Products of Oil and Gas
Depicts many of the products made from oil and gas.
Availability: Single copies to schools in the United States.
Suggested Grade: 4-12
Order Number: order by title
Format: Poster; 10 x 17 inches
Source: Ohio Oil & Gas Energy Education Program
P. O. Box 187
Granville, OH 43023
Phone: 1-740-587-0410
Fax: 1-740-587-0446
World Wide Web URL: http://www.oogeep.org
Email Address: rreda@oogeep.org

Quiz Hub
Age-appropriate learning activities are found here that cover music, science, social studies, math, and more.
Availability: All requesters
Suggested Grade: 3-8
Order Number: not applicable
Format: Web Site
Source: Dyann Schmidel and Wanda Wojcik
World Wide Web URL:
http://quizhub.com/quiz/quizhub.cfm

Rainbow Raccoons, The
Four brightly colored raccoons invite kids to learn about health, science, history, and more.
Availability: All requesters
Suggested Grade: preK-4
Order Number: not applicable
Format: Web Site
Source: Rainbow Raccoons
World Wide Web URL: http://www.rainbowraccoons.com/

Reasons for Seasons, The
A collection of sixty power point slides that explain the changing of the seasons.
Availability: All requesters
Suggested Grade: 6-12
Order Number: not applicable
Production Date: 2005

Format: Power Point Presentation
Source: Edward M. Murphy
World Wide Web URL:
http://www.astro.virginia.edu/SST/resources/
The%20Seasons.pdf

Safe Science
Learn more about creating a safe science laboratory.
Availability: All requesters
Suggested Grade: 8
Order Number: not applicable
Format: WebQuest
Source: John K. Hall
World Wide Web URL:
http://www.kayenta.k12.az.us/KMS/webquest/safescience/

School Testing--Behind the Numbers
A lively, humorous and thoughtful discussion of the meaning and impact of school testing.
Availability: All requesters
Suggested Grade: 7-Adult
Order Number: not applicable
Production Date: 2002
Format: Streaming Video
Terms: A simple FREE registration is required to view videos.
Source: Annenberg Media
World Wide Web URL:
http://www.learner.org/resources/browse.html

Sciencebase.com
Numerous science articles on all sorts of topics in the field.
Availability: All requesters
Suggested Grade: 9-Adult
Order Number: not applicable
Format: Online Articles
Source: David Bradley
World Wide Web URL: http://sciencebase.com/

ScienceDaily Magazine
Here you will find the latest science research news.
Availability: All requesters
Suggested Grade: 7-Adult
Order Number: not applicable
Format: Web Site
Source: ScienceDaily Magazine
World Wide Web URL: http://www.sciencedaily.com/

Science Fair Home Page
A project of the Eastern Newfoundland Science Fairs Council, this site lists hundreds of topics for science fair projects. Broken down by grade level and subject.
Availability: All requesters
Suggested Grade: All ages
Order Number: not applicable
Format: Web Site
Source: Science Fairs
World Wide Web URL:
http://www.stemnet.nf.ca/sciencefairs/

Science Fairs in Elementary School

Helpful information for conducting a science fair at the elementary level.

Availability: All requesters
Suggested Grade: Teacher Reference
Order Number: not applicable
Production Date: 1998
Format: Online Article

Source: Andrea K. Balas
World Wide Web URL:
http://www.apples4theteacher.com/resources/
modules.php?op=modload&name=
News&file=article&sid=72

Science Jokes

Q. What did one lab rat say to the other? A. "I've got my scientists so well trained that every time I push the buzzer, he brings me a snack." This is just one of more than 2500 jokes and quizzes found here.

Availability: All requesters
Suggested Grade: 6-Adult
Order Number: not applicable
Format: Web Site

Source: Joachim Verhagen
World Wide Web URL:
http://www.xs4all.nl/~jcdverha/scijokes/

Science Role Plays

An interesting experiment in which students role play the scientific processes.

Availability: All requesters
Suggested Grade: 5-8
Order Number: not applicable
Format: Online Lesson Plan

Source: Janet Weaver
World Wide Web URL:
http://www.col-ed.org/cur/sci/sci175.txt

Science Screen Report for Kids

An award winning science videotape series provided free of charge to schools nationwide through corporate sponsorship. Seven new and exciting titles covering various disciplines are produced each year. The videos are designed as curriculum enhancement. Materials address National Science Standards as well as science literacy benchmarks.

Availability: Schools and school districts in the United States and Canada.
Suggested Grade: 1-6
Order Number: order by title
Format: DVD
Special Notes: **Becomes permanent property of the school or district.**

Source: Science Screen Report
Mr. Scott Forman, Corporate Relations
1000 Clint Moore Road
Boca Raton, FL 33487
Phone: 1-800-232-2133, ext. 201
Email Address: 2scott@ssrvideo.com

Science Screen Report

An award winning science videotape series provided free of charge to schools nationwide through corporate sponsorship. Seven new and exciting titles covering various disciplines are produced each year. The videos are designed as curriculum enhancement. and include teacher's guides and review sheets. The goal of the program is to encourage continued studies in the sciences while helping students develop an interest in pursuing a science and technology related career. Materials address National Science Standards as well as science literacy benchmarks.

Availability: Schools and school districts in the United States and Canada.
Suggested Grade: 6-12
Order Number: order by title
Format: DVD
Special Notes: **Becomes permanent property of the school or district.**

Source: Science Screen Report
Mr. Scott Forman, Corporate Relations
1000 Clint Moore Road
Boca Raton, FL 33487
Phone: 1-800-232-2133, ext. 201
Email Address: 2scott@ssrvideo.com

Science Toys You Can Make With Your Kids

Describes in simple terms how to make toys that teach science.

Availability: All requesters
Suggested Grade: All ages
Order Number: not applicable
Format: Online Book

Source: Simon Quellen Field
World Wide Web URL: http://sci-toys.com/index.html

Science Whatzit!

Provides answers to many, many science questions.

Availability: All requesters
Suggested Grade: All ages
Order Number: not applicable
Format: Web Site

Source: Oregon Museum of Science and Industry
World Wide Web URL:
http://www.omsi.org/explore/whatzit/

Sci4Kids

Information about what scientists do and what discoveries they have made.

Availability: All requesters
Suggested Grade: 2-7
Order Number: not applicable
Format: Web Site

Source: Agricultural Research Service
World Wide Web URL:
http://www.ars.usda.gov/is/kids/sci4kids.htm

 Indicates an Internet Resource--just enter the URL and instantly access the FREE teaching aid you need!
All materials listed in this 2010-2011 edition are BRAND NEW!

61

GENERAL SCIENCE

SCIMEDIA: Hypermedia Index
Definitions to all sorts of scientific terms.
Availability: All requesters
Suggested Grade: 9-Adult
Order Number: not applicable
Format: Online Glossary
Source: Science Hypermedia, Inc.
World Wide Web URL:
http://elchem.kaist.ac.kr/vt/chem-ed/scidex.htm

Shoe Box Archaeology
Teach children the value of our past and the past of other people of the world by deciphering various indicators.
Availability: All requesters
Suggested Grade: 4-8
Order Number: not applicable
Format: Online Lesson Plan
Source: Johanna Hadden
World Wide Web URL:
http://www.col-ed.org/cur/sst/sst71.txt

So Why Should I Care?
Explore some areas skimmed over in high school math and science.
Availability: All requesters
Suggested Grade: 9-12
Order Number: not applicable
Format: Web Site
Special Notes: This URL will lead you to a subject page. Then click on the appropriate subject heading.
Source: ThinkQuest
World Wide Web URL:
http://www.thinkquest.org/pls/html/think.library

SparkNotes
A collection of online study guides for literature, mathematics, science, and many other topics.
Availability: All requesters
Suggested Grade: 9-12
Order Number: not applicable
Format: Online Study Guides
Source: iTurf Inc.
World Wide Web URL: http://www.sparknotes.com

Taconite Pellet Kit
Samples of rock, concentrate, and iron pellets used to make steel.
Availability: Available while supplies last to schools, libraries, and homeschoolers in the United States and Canada.
Suggested Grade: All ages
Order Number: order by title
Format: Samples
Source: Iron Mining Association of Minnesota
324 West Superior Street, Suite 502
Duluth, MN 55802
World Wide Web URL:
www.taconite.orghttp://www.taconite.org

Taconite Rocks!
A downloadable curriculum that details the history, and uses, of taconite and the taconite industry.
Availability: All requesters
Suggested Grade: 6
Order Number: not applicable
Format: Downloadable Curriculum
Source: Iron Mining Association of Minnesota
World Wide Web URL:
http://www.taconite.org/curriculum.pdf

Teacher's Oil & Gas Educational Packet
Lots of materials with information about oil and gas, activities, and resources.
Availability: Single copies to schools and libraries in the United States.
Suggested Grade: 4-12
Order Number: order by title
Format: Packet of Materials
Source: Ohio Oil & Gas Energy Education Program
P. O. Box 187
Granville, OH 43023
Phone: 1-740-587-0410
Fax: 1-740-587-0446
World Wide Web URL: http://www.oogeep.org
Email Address: rreda@oogeep.org

Temperature and Water Density
Teaches students about the density of water as it relates to temperature and helps them identify the forces governing convection in liquids.
Availability: All requesters
Suggested Grade: 7-8
Order Number: not applicable
Format: Online Lesson Plan
Source: Steve McFarland
World Wide Web URL:
http://www.col-ed.org/cur/sci/sci212.txt

Thinking Fountain
Presents ideas from A to Z for science lessons, activities, and resources.
Availability: All requesters
Suggested Grade: All ages
Order Number: not applicable
Format: Web Site
Source: Science Museum of Minnesota
World Wide Web URL:
http://www.smm.org/sln/tf/nav/thinkingfountain.html

Ultimate Science Fair Resource, The
All the information you need for conducting or participating in a science fair.
Availability: All requesters
Suggested Grade: All ages
Order Number: not applicable
Format: Web Site

Source: Society for Amateur Scientists
World Wide Web URL: http://www.scifair.org/

Using Microscopes
Teaches students how to use a microscope, while also studying cells.

Availability:	All requesters
Suggested Grade:	3-6
Order Number:	not applicable
Format:	Online Lesson Plan

Source: Theresa Figarelli
World Wide Web URL:
http://www.col-ed.org/cur/sci/sci06.txt

Visualize Everyday Metric Units
Provides illustrations which show a frame-of-reference method for learning to use the metric system.

Availability:	All requesters.
Suggested Grade:	3-Adult
Order Number:	not applicableJune 27, 2010
Format:	Downloadable Article

Source: U. S. Metric Association, Inc.
World Wide Web URL: http://www.metric.org

Water Cycle
Evaporation, condensation, and the effects of the water cycle on the climate and the land are closely examined.

Availability:	Schools, libraries, homeschoolers, and nursing homes in Illinois, Indiana, Iowa, Michigan, Minnesota, Missouri, Ohio, and Wisconsin only.
Suggested Grade:	9-12
Order Number:	400
Format:	VHS videotape
Terms:	Return postage is paid by borrower. Book 10-14 days in advance. Return 7 days after showing. Please provide alternate showing date.

Source: U. S. Fish and Wildlife Service
Region 3, Resource Library, 3815 American Boulevard
Bloomington, MN 55425
Fax: 1-612-725-3279
Email Address: judy_geck@fws.gov

Water Cycle: Saving An Ancient Lake
The video focuses on Mono Lake, a place of unworldly beauty in the desert of eastern California. Mono Lake is believed to be the oldest continually existing lake in North America.

Availability:	Schools, libraries, homeschoolers, and nursing homes in Illinois, Indiana, Iowa, Michigan, Minnesota, Missouri, Ohio, and Wisconsin only.
Suggested Grade:	5-12
Order Number:	198
Format:	VHS videotape
Terms:	Return postage is paid by borrower. Book 10-14 days in advance. Return 7 days after showing. Please provide alternate showing date.

Source: U. S. Fish and Wildlife Service
Region 3, Resource Library
3815 American Boulevard
Bloomington, MN 55425
Fax: 1-612-725-3279
Email Address: judy_geck@fws.gov

Water: Who Needs It?
Answers this question.

Availability:	Schools, libraries, homeschoolers, and nursing homes in the United States.
Suggested Grade:	K-6
Order Number:	order by title
Format:	DVD
Special Notes:	A number of titles from this organization are included on this DVD.
Terms:	Borrower pays return postage. Return within 14 days after scheduled use, via UPS or Federal Express. Book at least 14 days in advance and include alternate date. Requests should include title(s), format, name of responsible person, organizational affiliation, phone, and complete delivery address. No part of any program can be used or duplicated without prior written permission. All programs are available for purchase at a nominal fee. May be available in other formats; inquire if interested. Online video previews are available.

Source: California Department of Water Resources
Attn: Video Library, Room 204-22
P. O. Box 942836
Sacramento, CA 94236-0001
Phone: 1-916-653-4893
Fax: 1-916-653-3310
World Wide Web URL: http://www.water.ca.gov/
Email Address: www.publicawillm@water.ca.gov

Water: Who Needs It?
Answers this question.

Availability:	Schools, libraries, homeschoolers, and nursing homes in the United States.
Suggested Grade:	K-6
Order Number:	order by title
Format:	VHS videotape
Terms:	Borrower pays return postage. Return within 14 days after scheduled use, via UPS or Federal Express. Book at least 14 days in advance and include alternate date. Requests should include title(s), format, name of responsible person, organizational affiliation, phone, and complete delivery address. No part of any program can be used or duplicated without prior written permission. All programs are available for purchase at a nominal fee. May be available in other formats; inquire if interested. Online video previews are available.

Source: California Department of Water Resources
Attn: Video Library, Room 204-22
P. O. Box 942836
Sacramento, CA 94236-0001
Phone: 1-916-653-4893
Fax: 1-916-653-3310

 Indicates an Internet Resource--just enter the URL and instantly access the FREE teaching aid you need!
All materials listed in this 2010-2011 edition are BRAND NEW!

63

World Wide Web URL: http://www.water.ca.gov/
Email Address: www.publicawillm@water.ca.gov

Welcome to Maya Adventure
Highlights science activities and information related to ancient and modern Maya culture.

Availability: All requesters
Suggested Grade: 4-12
Order Number: not applicable
Format: Web Site

Source: Science Museum of Minnesota (Maya)
World Wide Web URL: http://www.sci.mus.mn.us/sln/ma

Whiz Kid Activities Packet
Lots of activities for learning about science.

Availability: All requesters
Suggested Grade: 5-10
Order Number: not applicable
Format: Downloadable Activity Book

Source: Agricultural Research Service
World Wide Web URL:
http://www.ars.usda.gov/is/kids/teachers/WhizKidAct.htm

Wild Ones, The
In addition to finding information about endangered species and habitats, students can also post their own telecollaborative projects.

Availability: All requesters
Suggested Grade: K-8
Order Number: not applicable
Format: Web Site

Source: Michael Wilkinson
World Wide Web URL: http://www.thewildones.org/

Willo: The Dinosaur With a Heart
Learn what scientists have discovered from their study of Willow--a 66-million-year-old Thescelosaurus.

Availability: All requesters
Suggested Grade: All ages
Order Number: not applicable
Format: Web Site

Source: North Carolina Museum of Natural Sciences and
North Carolina State University
World Wide Web URL: http://www.dinoheart.org

Your Five Senses
Students discover the use of all their five senses and learn about the nervous system.

Availability: All requesters
Suggested Grade: K-12
Order Number: not applicable
Production Date: 2007
Format: Online Lesson Plan

Source: Miriam Lev
World Wide Web URL: http://www.educationworld.com/
a_tsl/archives/07-1/lesson010.shtml

Adaptations of Plants

This video shows how various plants are adapted for protection from plant-eating animals, and how seed plants are adapted for reproduction.

Availability: Schools, libraries, homeschoolers, and nursing homes in Illinois, Indiana, Iowa, Michigan, Minnesota, Missouri, Ohio, and Wisconsin only.
Suggested Grade: 9-12
Order Number: 2
Format: VHS videotape
Terms: Return postage is paid by borrower. Book 10-14 days in advance. Return 7 days after showing. Please provide alternate showing date.

Source: U. S. Fish and Wildlife Service
Region 3, Resource Library
3815 American Boulevard
Bloomington, MN 55425
Fax: 1-612-725-3279
Email Address: judy_geck@fws.gov

All Things Plant

The complexity of plant development from primitive, single celled organisms to the largest and oldest living things on earth is explored by the camera in both live action and graphic animation, providing an understanding of the basic groups into which al plants are divided.

Availability: Schools, libraries, homeschoolers, and nursing homes in Illinois, Indiana, Iowa, Michigan, Minnesota, Missouri, Ohio, and Wisconsin only.
Suggested Grade: 9-12
Order Number: 6
Format: VHS videotape
Terms: Return postage is paid by borrower. Book 10-14 days in advance. Return 7 days after showing. Please provide alternate showing date.

Source: U. S. Fish and Wildlife Service
Region 3, Resource Library
3815 American Boulevard
Bloomington, MN 55425
Fax: 1-612-725-3279
Email Address: judy_geck@fws.gov

Alternatives to Animal Dissection in School Science Classes

Presents some alternatives to dissecting frogs.

Availability: All requesters
Suggested Grade: Teacher Reference
Order Number: not applicable
Production Date: 1996
Format: Online Article

Source: David L. Haury
World Wide Web URL:
http://www.ericdigests.org/1998-1/animal.htm

Anatomically Correct: The Online Cat Dissection

Identify organs, view labeled diagrams and download movies of actual dissection performed by a veterinarian.

Availability: All requesters
Suggested Grade: 9-12
Order Number: not applicable
Format: Web Site
Special Notes: This URL will lead you to a subject page. Then click on the appropriate subject heading.

Source: ThinkQuest
World Wide Web URL:
http://www.thinkquest.org/pls/html/think.library

Animal Life Spans

How long do animals usually live? What about dogs, elephants, big or small animals? What are some factors that influence life span? Shows how scientists determine the age of animals in the wild. Using long- and short-lived animals, concludes that environment, size, food, shelter, a place to have and care for young, number of babies, and maturity rate all affect an animal's life span.

Availability: Schools, libraries, and homeschoolers in the United States who serve the hearing impaired.
Suggested Grade: 4-8
Order Number: 12979
Production Date: 1992
Format: DVD
Special Notes: Produced by National Geographic Society.
Terms: Sponsor pays all transportation costs. Return one week after receipt. Participation is limited to deaf or hard of hearing Americans, their parents, families, teachers, counselors, or others whose use would benefit a deaf or hard of hearing person. Only one person in the audience needs to be hearing impaired. You must register--which is free. These videos are all open-captioned--no special equipment is required for viewing.

Source: Described and Captioned Media Program
National Association of the Deaf
4211 Church Street Ext.
Roebuck, SC 29376
Phone: 1-800-237-6213
Fax: 1-800-538-5636
World Wide Web URL: http://www.dcmp.org

Animal Migration

Why do animals migrate? They migrate to find food, to escape seasonal changes, and to breed. Whales swim from the Arctic to give birth in warm Mexican waters. Bats migrate each spring to specific caves. Wildebeests constantly migrate to find food. Monarch butterflies take several generations to complete a seasonal migration. Whether daily, seasonal, annual, or only twice, migration remains a spectacular and mysterious event.

Availability: Schools, libraries, and homeschoolers in the United States who serve the hearing impaired.
Suggested Grade: 4-8
Order Number: 12980
Production Date: 1993
Format: DVD
Special Notes: Produced by National Geographic Society.

 Indicates an Internet Resource--just enter the URL and instantly access the FREE teaching aid you need!
All materials listed in this 2010-2011 edition are BRAND NEW!

65

Terms: Sponsor pays all transportation costs. Return one week after receipt. Participation is limited to deaf or hard of hearing Americans, their parents, families, teachers, counselors, or others whose use would benefit a deaf or hard of hearing person. Only one person in the audience needs to be hearing impaired. You must register--which is free. These videos are all open-captioned--no special equipment is required for viewing.

Source: Described and Captioned Media Program
National Association of the Deaf
4211 Church Street Ext.
Roebuck, SC 29376
Phone: 1-800-237-6213
Fax: 1-800-538-5636
World Wide Web URL: http://www.dcmp.org

Behavior of Ants, The

Students will use the steps of the Scientific Method to independently develop and test their own ideas through experimentation with ants.

Availability:	All requesters
Suggested Grade:	5-8
Order Number:	not applicable
Format:	Online Lesson Plan

Source: David Shindelman
World Wide Web URL:
http://biology.arizona.edu/sciconn/lessons2/shindelman/
Objectives.htm

Biocomplexity

Defines biocomplexity, characteristics, types of studies, case studies, and future research.

Availability:	All requesters
Suggested Grade:	6-Adult
Order Number:	not applicable
Format:	Online Fact Sheet

Source: Ecological Society of America, The
World Wide Web URL:
http://www.esa.org/education_diversity/factsheets.php

Biodiversity

Defines biodiversity and explains what threatens it, why it is important, and what ecologists are doing to better understand it.

Availability:	All requesters
Suggested Grade:	6-Adult
Order Number:	not applicable
Format:	Online Fact Sheet

Source: Ecological Society of America, The
World Wide Web URL:
http://www.esa.org/education_diversity/factsheets.php

Blood, Heart and Circulation

The heart is a pump, moving blood throughout the body via arteries and veins. Uses graphics to clarify the circulatory system and its functions. Notes the effects of exercise, nutrition, smoking, and infections on this system, and briefly illustrates coagulation, nosebleeds, and vaccinations.

Availability:	Schools, libraries, and homeschoolers in the United States who serve the hearing impaired.
Suggested Grade:	4-8
Order Number:	12896
Format:	DVD
Special Notes:	Also available as live streaming video over the Internet.

Terms: Sponsor pays all transportation costs. Return one week after receipt. Participation is limited to deaf or hard of hearing Americans, their parents, families, teachers, counselors, or others whose use would benefit a deaf or hard of hearing person. Only one person in the audience needs to be hearing impaired. You must register--which is free. These videos are all open-captioned--no special equipment is required for viewing.

Source: Described and Captioned Media Program
National Association of the Deaf
4211 Church Street Ext.
Roebuck, SC 29376
Phone: 1-800-237-6213
Fax: 1-800-538-5636
World Wide Web URL: http://www.dcmp.org

Body Image for Boys

Discusses how young men see themselves and examines the growing phenomena of increasing gym memberships, exercise addiction, and more.

Availability:	Schools, libraries, and homeschoolers in the United States who serve the hearing impaired.
Suggested Grade:	6-12
Order Number:	11648
Production Date:	2002
Format:	DVD
Special Notes:	Also available as live streaming video over the Internet.

Terms: Sponsor pays all transportation costs. Return one week after receipt. Participation is limited to deaf or hard of hearing Americans, their parents, families, teachers, counselors, or others whose use would benefit a deaf or hard of hearing person. Only one person in the audience needs to be hearing impaired. You must register--which is free. These videos are all open-captioned--no special equipment is required for viewing.

Source: Described and Captioned Media Program
National Association of the Deaf
4211 Church Street Ext.
Roebuck, SC 29376
Phone: 1-800-237-6213
Fax: 1-800-538-5636
World Wide Web URL: http://www.dcmp.org

Bone Names

Explains the history behind the names given to our bones.

Availability:	One copy to schools, libraries, and homeschoolers world-wide. May be copied.
Suggested Grade:	7-12
Order Number:	Vol. 38, No. 1
Production Date:	2003
Format:	Article
Special Notes:	May also be downloaded from the web site.

Source: Kansas School Naturalist, The
Department of Biology, Box 4050
Emporia State University
Emporia, KS 66801-5087
Phone: 1-620-341-5614
Fax: 1-620-341-5607
World Wide Web URL:
www.emporia.edu/ksn/http://www.emporia.edu/ksn/
Email Address: ksnaturl@emporia.edu

Botany Online
An online book covering plant anatomy, genetics, organic chemistry and much more.

Availability: All requesters
Suggested Grade: 9-Adult
Languages: English; German
Order Number: not applicable
Format: Online Book

Source: Peter V. Sengbusch
World Wide Web URL:
http://www.biologie.uni-hamburg.de/
b-online/e00/contents.htm

BrainsRule!
Learn about the brain.

Availability: All requesters
Suggested Grade: 3-5; 6-8
Order Number: not applicable
Format: Web Site

Source: University of Nebraska and the University of Texas
World Wide Web URL: http://www.brainsrule.com/

Brain, The: The First Computer
The human brain is often compared to a computer, but this three-pound organ is far more complex, and capable than the most advanced computer. Everything we do, are, think, and feel begins with the brain. Defines the parts and functions of a brain cell, explores how the brain works, and mentions brain chemicals.

Availability: Schools, libraries, and homeschoolers in the United States who serve the hearing impaired.
Suggested Grade: 4-8
Order Number: 24042
Format: DVD
Special Notes: Also available as live streaming video over the Internet.
Terms: Sponsor pays all transportation costs. Return one week after receipt. Participation is limited to deaf or hard of hearing Americans, their parents, families, teachers, counselors, or others whose use would benefit a deaf or hard of hearing person. Only one person in the audience needs to be hearing impaired. You must register--which is free. These videos are all open-captioned--no special equipment is required for viewing.

Source: Described and Captioned Media Program
National Association of the Deaf
4211 Church Street Ext.
Roebuck, SC 29376
Phone: 1-800-237-6213

Fax: 1-800-538-5636
World Wide Web URL: http://www.dcmp.org

Breath of Life
During an average lifetime, enough air passes through our lungs to fill a football stadium. Examines the complex process of respiration, beginning with the air's entrance into the nose. Explores the oxygen-carbon dioxide exchange in the lungs and the importance of oxygen in the blood to the body's tissues. Microphotography of the respiratory system reveals the secrets of the breath of life.

Availability: Schools, libraries, and homeschoolers in the United States who serve the hearing impaired.
Suggested Grade: 9-12
Order Number: 13072
Production Date: 1994
Format: DVD
Terms: Sponsor pays all transportation costs. Return one week after receipt. Participation is limited to deaf or hard of hearing Americans, their parents, families, teachers, counselors, or others whose use would benefit a deaf or hard of hearing person. Only one person in the audience needs to be hearing impaired. You must register--which is free. These videos are all open-captioned--no special equipment is required for viewing.

Source: Described and Captioned Media Program
National Association of the Deaf
4211 Church Street Ext.
Roebuck, SC 29376
Phone: 1-800-237-6213
Fax: 1-800-538-5636
World Wide Web URL: http://www.dcmp.org

Case for Creation, The
Experts present a compelling summary of scientific evidence for creation and against evolution. This summarizes the history of the creation vs. evolution debate in America from 1925 to present.

Availability: Public schools in the Continental United States. Others must pay a rental fee.
Suggested Grade: 5-Adult
Order Number: order by title
Production Date: 1992
Format: DVD
Terms: Borrower pays return postage. Provide alternate showing date. Return 30 days after scheduled showing date via U. S. Mail. The video must be ordered by a teacher, principal, or school administrator on school stationery.

Source: Eden Communications
P. O. Box 200
Gilbert, AZ 85299
Phone: 1-800-332-2261
Fax: 1-480-507-3623
World Wide Web URL: http://www.eden.org/schools
Email Address: orders@eden.org

Indicates an Internet Resource--just enter the URL and instantly access the FREE teaching aid you need!
All materials listed in this 2010-2011 edition are BRAND NEW!

67

Case for Creation, The

Experts present a compelling summary of scientific evidence for creation and against evolution. This summarizes the history of the creation vs. evolution debate in America from 1925 to present.

Availability: Public schools in the Continental United States. Others must pay a rental fee.
Suggested Grade: 5-Adult
Order Number: order by title
Production Date: 1992
Format: VHS videotape
Terms: Borrower pays return postage. Provide alternate showing date. Return 30 days after scheduled showing date via U. S. Mail. The video must be ordered by a teacher, principal, or school administrator on school stationery.

Source: Eden Communications
P. O. Box 200
Gilbert, AZ 85299
Phone: 1-800-332-2261
Fax: 1-480-507-3623
World Wide Web URL: http://www.eden.org/schools
Email Address: orders@eden.org

Cells Alive!!

Devoted to the study of cells.

Availability: All requesters
Suggested Grade: 4-12
Order Number: not applicable
Format: Web Site

Source: James A. Sullivan
World Wide Web URL: http://www.cellsalive.com/

Cells and Tissues

Uses microphotography and graphics and examines different kinds of plant and animal cells, discussing their structures and tissues.

Availability: Schools, libraries, and homeschoolers in the United States who serve the hearing impaired.
Suggested Grade: 9-Adult
Order Number: 12897
Format: DVD
Special Notes: Also available as live streaming video over the Internet.
Terms: Sponsor pays all transportation costs. Return one week after receipt. Participation is limited to deaf or hard of hearing Americans, their parents, families, teachers, counselors, or others whose use would benefit a deaf or hard of hearing person. Only one person in the audience needs to be hearing impaired. You must register--which is free. These videos are all open-captioned--no special equipment is required for viewing.

Source: Described and Captioned Media Program
National Association of the Deaf
4211 Church Street Ext.
Roebuck, SC 29376
Phone: 1-800-237-6213
Fax: 1-800-538-5636
World Wide Web URL: http://www.dcmp.org

Cells Are Us

Explains all about the cells that make up our bodies.

Availability: All requesters
Suggested Grade: 2-8
Order Number: not applicable
Format: Online Article
Special Notes: By Dr. Frank Balkwil and Mic Rolph.

Source: Imperial Cancer Research Fund
World Wide Web URL:
http://www.icnet.uk/kids/cellsrus/cellsrus.html

Changes of Puberty

A complete lesson about the changes the body goes through in puberty.

Availability: All requesters
Suggested Grade: 6-8
Order Number: not applicable
Format: Online Lesson Plan

Source: Marilyn Fenichel
World Wide Web URL:
http://school.discovery.com/lessonplans/programs/puberty/

Chemical Carousel: A Trip Around the Carbon Cycle

Illustrates photosynthesis and amino acid synthesis in a plant and protein synthesis in a cow.

Availability: All requesters
Suggested Grade: 4-12
Order Number: not applicable
Format: Web Site
Special Notes: This URL will lead you to a subject page. Then click on the appropriate subject heading.

Source: ThinkQuest
World Wide Web URL:
http://www.thinkquest.org/pls/html/think.library

Classifying Plants and Animals

Explains the system by which biologists classify plants and animals. Film shows why such a system is needed and traces the development of the modern system of classification.

Availability: Schools, libraries, homeschoolers, and nursing homes in Illinois, Indiana, Iowa, Michigan, Minnesota, Missouri, Ohio, and Wisconsin only.
Suggested Grade: 9-12
Order Number: 44
Format: VHS videotape
Terms: Return postage is paid by borrower. Book 10-14 days in advance. Return 7 days after showing. Please provide alternate showing date.

Source: U. S. Fish and Wildlife Service
Region 3, Resource Library
3815 American Boulevard
Bloomington, MN 55425
Fax: 1-612-725-3279
Email Address: judy_geck@fws.gov

Cloning: You're Not Seeing Double!

Learn about genetics and cloning.

Availability: All requesters
Suggested Grade: 6-12
Order Number: not applicable
Format: Web Site
Special Notes: This URL will lead you to a subject page.
                  Then click on the appropriate subject heading.

Source: ThinkQuest
World Wide Web URL:
http://www.thinkquest.org/pls/html/think.library

Cornea and Corneal Disease

Describes the cornea's structure and function. Provides information on common corneal diseases.

Availability: All requesters
Suggested Grade: 4-Adult
Order Number: not applicable
Format: Downloadable Fact Sheet

Source: National Eye Institute
World Wide Web URL:
http://www.nei.nih.gov/health/cornealdisease/

Creation or Evolution?

A college student tries to shake the faith of his father in the Bible's account of creation, but fails and discovers scientific and historical fact that is documented as thoroughly as the facts of "science."

Availability: Schools, libraries, homeschoolers, and nursing homes in the United States and Canada.
Suggested Grade: 7-12
Order Number: 02
Format: DVD
Special Notes: Cleared for TV broadcast.
Terms: Borrower pays return postage. Book one month in advance. Return within 60 days after scheduled use, via U.S. Mail, Library Rate. Loan DVDs are available two at a time. Upon return of the borrowed DVD, another will be sent automatically, unless otherwise requested. For each title, borrowers must use both title and identifying number. Book at least 3 weeks in advance. Can be purchased for $6.00 (includes postage and handling)--send check or money order.

Source: Dawn Video Services
4804 Laurel Canyon Blvd., 724
Valley Village, CA 91607
Phone: 1-888-440-3296
Fax: 1-818-762-9428
World Wide Web URL: http://www.dawnbible.com/

Creation vs. Evolution

A scientific and religious presentation showing that our origins must have come from an intelligent creator. Answers the questions of why we are here and what is our destiny.

Availability: Schools, libraries, homeschoolers, churches, and nursing homes in the United States.
Suggested Grade: 6-Adult
Order Number: order by title
Format: DVD

Special Notes: **May be retained permanently.**
Terms: Book 2 to 3 weeks in advance.

Source: Chicago Bible Students
Jeannine Farrell
310 South Lambert Road
Glen Ellyn, IL 60137
Email Address: jean9farrell@aol.com

Dandelion

Uses colorful time lapse photography to trace the life cycle of the dandelion from seedling to seed producer, learn how insects spread pollen and about the dandelion's reaction to sunlight.

Availability: Schools, libraries, homeschoolers, and nursing homes in Illinois, Indiana, Iowa, Michigan, Minnesota, Missouri, Ohio, and Wisconsin only.
Suggested Grade: 6-12
Order Number: 328
Format: VHS videotape
Terms: Return postage is paid by borrower. Book 10-14 days in advance. Return 7 days after showing. Please provide alternate showing date.

Source: U. S. Fish and Wildlife Service
Region 3, Resource Library
3815 American Boulevard
Bloomington, MN 55425
Fax: 1-612-725-3279
Email Address: judy_geck@fws.gov

Digestion: Food to Energy

Traces how food is digested into nutrients that are absorbed by the human body to keep it healthy. Also, it discusses the key digestive organs and their functions, and presents some advice on proper nutrition and disease prevention.

Availability: Staff at schools with NET, WIC, CSFP, FDPIR, CACFP, UMD or Child Nutrition Program food programs in the United States. Those not having such an affiliation should contact their library to place an interlibrary loan request.
Suggested Grade: preK-6
Order Number: NAL Video 1020
Format: VHS videotape
Terms: Borrower pays return postage. RETURN the day after scheduled use. Book at least 4 weeks in advance. Requests must include your name, phone, mail address, eligibility program, title, NAL number, show date, and a statement, "I have read the warning on copyright restrictions and accept full responsibility for compliance." One title per request.

Source: National Agricultural Library
Document Delivery Services Branch
4th Floor, Photo Lab, 10301 Baltimore Avenue
Beltsville, MD 20705-2351
Phone: 1-301-504-5994
Fax: 1-301-504-5675
World Wide Web URL: http://www.nal.usda.gov/fnic
Email Address: lending@nal.usda.gov

 Indicates an Internet Resource--just enter the URL and instantly access the FREE teaching aid you need!
*All materials listed in this 2010-2011 edition are **BRAND NEW!***

69

DNA on the Internet
Genes, DNA, and chromosomes. Study who we are and why we are the way we are.

Availability:	All requesters
Suggested Grade:	9-12
Order Number:	not applicable
Format:	Web Site
Special Notes:	This URL will lead you to a subject page. Then click on the appropriate subject heading.

Source: ThinkQuest
World Wide Web URL:
http://www.thinkquest.org/pls/html/think.library

Dream Forest
Anna, a young girl from Holland, has moved to Colorado where she meets a friendly raccoon who takes her off into the mountains to meet his animal friends. In a dream sequence, messages on caring for animals and animal welfare are presented.

Availability:	Schools, libraries, homeschoolers, and nursing homes in Illinois, Indiana, Iowa, Michigan, Minnesota, Missouri, Ohio, and Wisconsin only.
Suggested Grade:	K-3
Order Number:	330
Format:	VHS videotape
Terms:	Return postage is paid by borrower. Book 10-14 days in advance. Return 7 days after showing. Please provide alternate showing date.

Source: U. S. Fish and Wildlife Service
Region 3, Resource Library
3815 American Boulevard
Bloomington, MN 55425
Fax: 1-612-725-3279
Email Address: judy_geck@fws.gov

Eggs
After gathering eggs from the hen house, Jeffrey and Kate learn about the parts of an egg and what each part does. Experiments with eggs show how strong they are and how weak they can become.

Availability:	Schools, libraries, and homeschoolers in the United States who serve the hearing impaired.
Suggested Grade:	2-6
Order Number:	12383
Production Date:	1994
Format:	DVD
Special Notes:	Produced by Films for the Humanities & Sciences.
Terms:	Sponsor pays all transportation costs. Return one week after receipt. Participation is limited to deaf or hard of hearing Americans, their parents, families, teachers, counselors, or others whose use would benefit a deaf or hard of hearing person. Only one person in the audience needs to be hearing impaired. You must register--which is free. These videos are all open-captioned--no special equipment is required for viewing.

Source: Described and Captioned Media Program
National Association of the Deaf
4211 Church Street Ext.
Roebuck, SC 29376
Phone: 1-800-237-6213
Fax: 1-800-538-5636
World Wide Web URL: http://www.dcmp.org

Eskeletons
Gives students the opportunity to study human anatomy while comparing it to the anatomy of a baboon or gorilla.

Availability:	All requesters
Suggested Grade:	6-Adult
Order Number:	not applicable
Format:	Web Site

Source: John Kappelman
World Wide Web URL: http://www.eskeletons.org/

Especially for Teens---Menstruation
Explains this function of the female body.

Availability:	Single copies to schools, libraries, and homeschoolers world-wide. It is preferred the requests be sent via email, fax, or phone.
Suggested Grade:	5-Adult
Order Number:	AP049
Production Date:	2007
Format:	Brochure
Special Notes:	Email requests only. Don't forgot to include complete mailing address.

Source: American College of Obstetricians and
Gynecologists, The
Resource Center
409 12th Street, S. W.
Washington, DC 20024
World Wide Web URL: http://www.acog.org
Email Address: resources@acog.org

Five Senses
Activities and lessons for teaching about the five senses.

Availability:	All requesters
Suggested Grade:	1-4
Order Number:	not applicable
Format:	Online Activities

Source: Southwest Educational Development Laboratory
World Wide Web URL:
http://www.sedl.org/scimath/pasopartners/senses/
welcome.html

Flowering Plant Diversity
An online lesson about plants.

Availability:	All requesters
Suggested Grade:	9-Adult
Order Number:	not applicable
Format:	Online Article

Source: Sean Carrington
World Wide Web URL:
http://scitec.uwichill.edu.bb/bcs/bl14apl/flow2.htm

Food Chains: A Bond of Life

Provides a basic understanding of how plants use the sun's energy to grow and how plants in turn provide food for animals. Explains the producer and consumer relationship.

Availability: Schools, libraries, homeschoolers, and nursing homes in Illinois, Indiana, Iowa, Michigan, Minnesota, Missouri, Ohio, and Wisconsin only.
Suggested Grade: 5-12
Order Number: 70
Format: VHS videotape
Terms: Return postage is paid by borrower. Book 10-14 days in advance. Return 7 days after showing. Please provide alternate showing date.

Source: U. S. Fish and Wildlife Service
Region 3, Resource Library
3815 American Boulevard
Bloomington, MN 55425
Fax: 1-612-725-3279
Email Address: judy_geck@fws.gov

Food From the Sun

Demonstrations and drawings show how life on earth relies on the sun for energy. Describes the basic processes by which plants and animals obtain the sun's energy, stored in food, and how this energy is converted into food.

Availability: Schools, libraries, homeschoolers, and nursing homes in Illinois, Indiana, Iowa, Michigan, Minnesota, Missouri, Ohio, and Wisconsin only.
Suggested Grade: 7-12
Order Number: 304
Production Date: 1967
Format: VHS videotape
Terms: Return postage is paid by borrower. Book 10-14 days in advance. Return 7 days after showing. Please provide alternate showing date.

Source: U. S. Fish and Wildlife Service
Region 3, Resource Library
3815 American Boulevard
Bloomington, MN 55425
Fax: 1-612-725-3279
Email Address: judy_geck@fws.gov

Froguts.com

Interactive frog dissection.
Availability: All requesters
Suggested Grade: 6-12
Order Number: not applicable
Format: Web Site

Source: Richard Hill
World Wide Web URL: http://www.froguts.com/

Future Is Wild, The

Based on the book of the same name, this project asks students to predict how a species population might evolve due to the Earth's changing climate.

Availability: All requesters
Suggested Grade: 10
Order Number: not applicable
Format: Online Lesson Plan

Source: Debbie Whittington
World Wide Web URL:
http://www.eduref.org/Virtual/Lessons/Science/
Animals/ANM0211.html

Genetic Science Learning Center

Activities and information about genetics.
Availability: All requesters
Suggested Grade: 3-5
Order Number: not applicable
Format: Web Site

Source: Genetic Science Learning Center
World Wide Web URL: http://gslc.genetics.utah.edu/

High School Biology Textbooks Do Not Meet National Standards

Explains the conclusions of a recent study by Project 2061, the ongoing science and mathematics education reform effort of the American Association for the Advancement of Science.

Availability: All requesters
Suggested Grade: Teacher Reference
Order Number: not applicable
Production Date: 2000
Format: Online Article

Source: David L. Haury
World Wide Web URL:
http://www.ericdigests.org/2003-1/biology.htm

Human Anatomy Online

Here is a great reference for students studying human anatomy and for those who just want to know more about the medical descriptions commonly used by doctors and nurses.

Availability: All requesters
Suggested Grade: 6-12
Order Number: not applicable
Format: Online Tutorial

Source: Inner Learning On-line
World Wide Web URL:
http://www.innerbody.com/http://www.innerbody.com/

Human Body

Presents seven major body systems and tells how they work.
Availability: All requesters
Suggested Grade: 6-12
Order Number: not applicable
Format: Web Site
Special Notes: This URL will lead you to a subject page. Then click on the appropriate subject heading.

Source: ThinkQuest
World Wide Web URL:
http://www.thinkquest.org/pls/html/think.library

 Indicates an Internet Resource--just enter the URL and instantly access the FREE teaching aid you need!
All materials listed in this 2010-2011 edition are BRAND NEW!

71

Human Pump, The

Blood, river of life and garbage collector of the body's cells, is pumped around the body in less than a minute by the heart. Discusses the composition of both blood and the heart. Microphotography offers a detailed view of the pumping heart and the circulatory system.

Availability: Schools, libraries, and homeschoolers in the United States who serve the hearing impaired.

Suggested Grade: 9-12
Order Number: 13084
Production Date: 1994
Format: DVD
Special Notes: Produced by Ambrose Video Publishing, Inc..
Terms: Sponsor pays all transportation costs. Return one week after receipt. Participation is limited to deaf or hard of hearing Americans, their parents, families, teachers, counselors, or others whose use would benefit a deaf or hard of hearing person. Only one person in the audience needs to be hearing impaired. You must register--which is free. These videos are all open-captioned--no special equipment is required for viewing.

Source: Described and Captioned Media Program
National Association of the Deaf
4211 Church Street Ext.
Roebuck, SC 29376
Phone: 1-800-237-6213
Fax: 1-800-538-5636
World Wide Web URL: http://www.dcmp.org

Kimball's Biology Pages

An online biology textbook.
Availability: All requesters
Suggested Grade: 9-Adult
Order Number: not applicable
Format: Online Book
Source: John W. Kimball
World Wide Web URL:
http://users.rcn.com/jkimball.ma.ultranet/BiologyPages/

Laboratory Safety Web Quest

A WebQuest for 10th grade biology students.
Availability: All requesters
Suggested Grade: 10
Order Number: not applicable
Format: WebQuest
Source: Celia Cox
World Wide Web URL:
http://www.tangischools.org/schools/phs/techno/slu/EDUC67
6/wequests/ceiliac/WQLab%20Safety.htm

Learning Programs for Biology

Provides photographs, animations, and information about biological organisms.
Availability: All requesters
Suggested Grade: 9-Adult
Order Number: not applicable
Format: Web Site
Source: BioMedia Associates
World Wide Web URL: http://ebiomedia.com/

Lesson Directory

Here are original peer-edited lessons, written by science educators, to specifically accompany peer-reviewed articles on this site.
Availability: All requesters
Suggested Grade: 6-12
Order Number: not applicable
Format: Online Lesson Plans
Source: American Institute of Biological Sciences
World Wide Web URL:
http://www.actionbioscience.org/lessondirectory.html

Let's Learn About Your Digestive System

This program discusses the basics of the normal human digestive system covering saliva and bile, the route the food takes through the body, and the various organs involved in digestion.
Availability: Staff at schools with NET, WIC, CSFP, FDPIR, CACFP, UMD or Child Nutrition Program food programs in the United States. Those not having such an affiliation should contact their library to place an interlibrary loan request.
Suggested Grade: 6-12
Order Number: NAL Video 1173
Production Date: 1990
Format: VHS videotape
Terms: Borrower pays return postage. RETURN the day after scheduled use. Book at least 4 weeks in advance. Requests must include your name, phone, mail address, eligibility program, title, NAL number, show date, and a statement, "I have read the warning on copyright restrictions and accept full responsibility for compliance." One title per request.

Source: National Agricultural Library
Document Delivery Services Branch
4th Floor, Photo Lab
10301 Baltimore Avenue
Beltsville, MD 20705-2351
Phone: 1-301-504-5994
Fax: 1-301-504-5675
World Wide Web URL: http://www.nal.usda.gov/fnic
Email Address: lending@nal.usda.gov

Looking at Fishes

This program observes the basic life processes of fish: reproduction, growth, excretion, respiration, and other adaptations for aquatic life.
Availability: Schools, libraries, homeschoolers, and nursing homes in Illinois, Indiana, Iowa, Michigan, Minnesota, Missouri, Ohio, and Wisconsin only.
Suggested Grade: 5-12
Order Number: 394
Format: VHS videotape
Terms: Return postage is paid by borrower. Book 10-14 days in advance. Return 7 days after showing. Please provide alternate showing date.

Source: U. S. Fish and Wildlife Service
Region 3, Resource Library
3815 American Boulevard
Bloomington, MN 55425
Fax: 1-612-725-3279
Email Address: judy_geck@fws.gov

Medical Dictionary Online

A searchable dictionary that contains terms relating to medical terminology, pharmaceutical drugs, healthcare equipment, health conditions, and more.

Availability: All requesters
Suggested Grade: 9-Adult
Order Number: not applicable
Format: Online Glossary
Source: Online-medical-dictionary.org
World Wide Web URL:
http://www.online-medical-dictionary.org/

Microorganism: Description, Uses, Diseases

Answers to questions about microorganisms. Interactive quiz.

Availability: All requesters
Suggested Grade: 4-12
Order Number: not applicable
Format: Web Site
Special Notes: This URL will lead you to a subject page. Then click on the appropriate subject heading.
Source: ThinkQuest
World Wide Web URL:
http://www.thinkquest.org/pls/html/think.library

Muscle Names

Identifies the more than 600 muscles of the human body.

Availability: One copy to schools, libraries, and homeschoolers world-wide. May be copied.
Suggested Grade: 5-Adult
Order Number: Vol. 42, No. 1
Production Date: 1995
Format: Article
Special Notes: May also be downloaded from the web site.
Source: Kansas School Naturalist, The
Department of Biology, Box 4050
Emporia State University
Emporia, KS 66801-5087
Phone: 1-620-341-5614
Fax: 1-620-341-5607
World Wide Web URL:
www.emporia.edu/ksn/http://www.emporia.edu/ksn/
Email Address: ksnaturl@emporia.edu

Neuroscience for Kids

This Web site provides lots of information for students and teachers who would like to learn more about the nervous system. Activities and experiments help teach about the brain and spinal cord.

Availability: All requesters
Suggested Grade: All ages

Order Number: not applicable
Format: Web Site
Source: Eric Chudler, Ph.D.
World Wide Web URL:
http://faculty.washington.edu/chudler/neurok.html

Neuroscience for Kids Newsletter

A newsletter, delivered right to your mailbox, to help students learn more about the brain and spinal cord.

Availability: All requesters
Suggested Grade: All ages
Order Number: not applicable
Format: Online Newsletter
Source: Eric Chudler, Ph.D.
World Wide Web URL:
http://faculty.washington.edu/chudler/neurok.html

Online Biology Book

Created by a seasoned biology teacher, this book is very detailed.

Availability: All requesters
Suggested Grade: 9-12
Order Number: not applicable
Format: Online Book
Source: M. J. Farabee
World Wide Web URL:
http://gened.emc.maricopa.edu/bio/bio181/BIOBK/
BioBookTOC.html

Open Heart

Hands-on activities to that how the heart works, how it gets into trouble, what can be done to rescue it, and what you can do to keep your heart healthy.

Availability: All requesters
Suggested Grade: 6-Adult
Order Number: not applicable
Format: Web Site
Special Notes: This file will open automatically on your computer.
Source: Columbus Medical Association Foundation
World Wide Web URL:
http://www.cosi.org/files/Flash/openHeart/heart.swf

Origin of Life, The

How did life begin? Did man evolve by accident from some primordial soup, or was there an intelligent designer? This program shows the results of scientists' ongoing attempts to produce life in the laboratory, and discusses DNA, the human brain, and many living things. Some scientists say there is evidence of intelligent design in the origin of life.

Availability: Public schools in the Continental United States. Others must pay a rental fee.
Suggested Grade: 5-Adult
Order Number: order by title
Format: DVD
Terms: Borrower pays return postage. Provide alternate showing date. Return 30 days after scheduled showing date via U. S. Mail. The video must be ordered by a

teacher, principal, or school administrator on school stationery.

Source: Eden Communications
P. O. Box 200
Gilbert, AZ 85299
Phone: 1-800-332-2261
Fax: 1-480-507-3623
World Wide Web URL: http://www.eden.org/schools
Email Address: orders@eden.org

Origin of Mankind, The

Did man evolve from ape-like ancestors? This program examines evidence for most of the current "missing links," exposing various common misconceptions and provides new perspective. This program suggests there is still little or no solid fossil evidence that man evolved from ape-like creatures.

Availability: Public schools in the Continental United States. Others must pay a rental fee.
Suggested Grade: 5-Adult
Order Number: order by title
Format: DVD
Terms: Borrower pays return postage.   Provide alternate showing date. Return 30 days after scheduled showing date via U. S. Mail. The video must be ordered by a teacher, principal, or school administrator on school stationery.

Source: Eden Communications
P. O. Box 200
Gilbert, AZ 85299
Phone: 1-800-332-2261
Fax: 1-480-507-3623
World Wide Web URL: http://www.eden.org/schools
Email Address: orders@eden.org

Origin of Species, The

Are all creatures branches of an evolutionary tree? Or are they all distinctly different, unique creations. What led Charles Darwin to the belief that one species could evolve into another? Today, scientists throughout the world are beginning to acknowledge what the Bible has stated so clearly for thousands of years. Living things cannot evolve upward by mutations, natural selection, or any other means.

Availability: Public schools in the Continental United States. Others must pay a rental fee.
Suggested Grade: 5-Adult
Order Number: order by title
Format: DVD
Special Notes: Part of the Origins: How the World Came to Be Series.
Terms: Borrower pays return postage.   Provide alternate showing date. Return 30 days after scheduled showing date via U. S. Mail. The video must be ordered by a teacher, principal, or school administrator on school stationery.

Source: Eden Communications
P. O. Box 200
Gilbert, AZ 85299

Phone: 1-800-332-2261
Fax: 1-480-507-3623
World Wide Web URL: http://www.eden.org/schools
Email Address: orders@eden.org

Origin of the Universe, The

This program reveals that the universe is far too complex and well-designed to have originated simply by time and chance. There is clear evidence of an intelligent "Master Designer." The cosmos is degenerating, not evolving upward. The Second Law of Thermodynamics is evidence that suggests design, not chance. Hosted by A.E. Wilder-Smith, Ph.D.

Availability: Public schools in the Continental United States. Others must pay a rental fee.
Suggested Grade: 5-Adult
Order Number: order by title
Format: DVD
Terms: Borrower pays return postage.   Provide alternate showing date. Return 30 days after scheduled showing date via U. S. Mail. The video must be ordered by a teacher, principal, or school administrator on school stationery.

Source: Eden Communications
P. O. Box 200
Gilbert, AZ 85299
Phone: 1-800-332-2261
Fax: 1-480-507-3623
World Wide Web URL: http://www.eden.org/schools
Email Address: orders@eden.org

Plant Biology for Non-Science Majors

Lecture notes for this three-credit course taught at the University of Maryland.

Availability: All requesters
Suggested Grade: 12-Adult
Order Number: not applicable
Format: Online Lecture Notes

Source: David Straney and Edgar Moctezuma
World Wide Web URL:
http://www.life.umd.edu/classroom/bsci124/main.html

Secrets of Plant Genomes: Revealed!

Explores how scientists doing plant genome research are unlocking the secrets of three important plants in our lives: corn, cotton, and potatoes.

Availability: Teachers, librarians, and group leaders in the United States.
Suggested Grade: 6-12
Order Number: order by title
Format: DVD
Special Notes: **May be retained permanently.**
Terms: It is asked that you complete a brief survey included with each program. Videos may not be duplicated--copies will be provided if you need them. Mail and FAX requests must be on school letterhead and contain a statement of total school enrollment, estimated number of student viewers, classes/subjects in which video is

used and audience grade level (must match audience specified in description). Allow at least four weeks for delivery.
Source: National Science Foundation
Please forward all requests on official letterhead to:
Video Placement Worldwide
25 Second Street North
St. Petersburg, FL 33701
Fax: 1-813-823-2955
World Wide Web URL: http://www.vpw.com

Seeing, Hearing, and Smelling the World
Explains all about the five senses.

Availability:	All requesters
Suggested Grade:	All ages
Languages:	English; Spanish
Order Number:	not applicable
Format:	Web Site or Downloadable Book

Source: Howard Hughes Medical Institute
World Wide Web URL: http://www.hhmi.org/senses/

Skeleton: Our Fantastic Framework
The skeleton, composed of many interconnecting living bones, gives the body shape and support. Red blood cells are made in the central layer, or marrow, of long bones. Joints, which connect bones, make movement possible. The bones in our hands and feet look similar, but have very different functions. When bones break, they must be protected and must receive good nutrition while they heal.

Availability:	Schools, libraries, and homeschoolers in the United States who serve the hearing impaired.
Suggested Grade:	4-7
Order Number:	2430
Production Date:	1988
Format:	DVD
Special Notes:	Produced by Thomas J Stanton Films.
Terms:	Sponsor pays all transportation costs. Return one week after receipt. Participation is limited to deaf or hard of hearing Americans, their parents, families, teachers, counselors, or others whose use would benefit a deaf or hard of hearing person. Only one person in the audience needs to be hearing impaired. You must register--which is free. These videos are all open-captioned--no special equipment is required for viewing.

Source: Described and Captioned Media Program
National Association of the Deaf
4211 Church Street Ext.
Roebuck, SC 29376
Phone: 1-800-237-6213
Fax: 1-800-538-5636
World Wide Web URL: http://www.dcmp.org

Soundry, The
Explains what sound is and how humans perceive it through the ear.

Availability:	All requesters
Suggested Grade:	6-12
Order Number:	not applicable
Format:	Web Site

Special Notes:	This URL will lead you to a subject page. Then click on the appropriate subject heading.

Source: ThinkQuest
World Wide Web URL:
http://www.thinkquest.org/pls/html/think.library

Starting Life
Where do baby animals come from? What do they look like? A family visits a farm in spring and learns the answers. Shows a duckling hatch and a lamb and calf being born. Viewers decide which creatures are born from eggs and which are born live. Later that spring, the family has a new baby.

Availability:	Schools, libraries, and homeschoolers in the United States who serve the hearing impaired.
Suggested Grade:	K-4
Order Number:	13025
Production Date:	1993
Format:	DVD
Special Notes:	Produced by ACG/United Learning.
Terms:	Sponsor pays all transportation costs. Return one week after receipt. Participation is limited to deaf or hard of hearing Americans, their parents, families, teachers, counselors, or others whose use would benefit a deaf or hard of hearing person. Only one person in the audience needs to be hearing impaired. You must register--which is free. These videos are all open-captioned--no special equipment is required for viewing.

Source: Described and Captioned Media Program
National Association of the Deaf
4211 Church Street Ext.
Roebuck, SC 29376
Phone: 1-800-237-6213
Fax: 1-800-538-5636
World Wide Web URL: http://www.dcmp.org

Tree of Life
Features more than 3,000 web pages about the "diversity of life on Earth, their evolutionary history (phylogeny), and characteristics." A wealth of information for biology teachers and students.

Availability:	All requesters
Suggested Grade:	9-12
Order Number:	not applicable
Format:	Web Site

Source: University of Arizona College of Agriculture and Life Sciences
World Wide Web URL:
http://tolweb.org/tree/phylogeny.html

Unraveling the Mysteries of the Eye
Information about how we see.

Availability:	All requesters
Suggested Grade:	6-12
Order Number:	not applicable
Format:	Web Site
Special Notes:	This URL will lead you to a subject page. Then click on the appropriate subject heading.

Indicates an Internet Resource--just enter the URL and instantly access the FREE teaching aid you need!
All materials listed in this 2010-2011 edition are BRAND NEW!

Source: ThinkQuest
World Wide Web URL:
http://www.thinkquest.org/pls/html/think.library

Visible Human Server, The

View the human anatomy in 3-D.

Availability: All requesters
Suggested Grade: 9-Adult
Order Number: not applicable
Format: Web Site

Source: Swiss Federal Institute of Technology
World Wide Web URL: http://visiblehuman.epfl.ch

Vision--A School Program for Grades 4-8

A series of three lessons to help students learn about the eye.

Availability: All requesters
Suggested Grade: 4-8
Order Number: not applicable
Format: Online Lesson Plans and Reproducible Handouts

Source: National Eye Institute
World Wide Web URL:
http://www.nei.nih.gov/education/visionschool/index.asp

Visit to the Feather River Hatchery, A

This video features Maria, who talks about her trip to the Fish Hatchery to her classmates in a "show and tell" format. It shows the hatchery and the life cycle of the salmon, as Maria tells of her experiences on the tour.

Availability: Schools, libraries, homeschoolers, and nursing homes in the United States.
Suggested Grade: 4-8
Order Number: order by title
Format: DVD
Special Notes: A number of titles from this organization are included on this DVD.
Terms: Borrower pays return postage. Return within 14 days after scheduled use, via UPS or Federal Express. Book at least 14 days in advance and include alternate date. Requests should include title(s), format, name of responsible person, organizational affiliation, phone, and complete delivery address. No part of any program can be used or duplicated without prior written permission. All programs are available for purchase at a nominal fee. May be available in other formats; inquire if interested. Online video previews are available.

Source: California Department of Water Resources
Attn: Video Library, Room 204-22
P. O. Box 942836
Sacramento, CA 94236-0001
Phone: 1-916-653-4893
Fax: 1-916-653-3310
World Wide Web URL: http://www.water.ca.gov/
Email Address: www.publicawillm@water.ca.gov

Visit to the Feather River Hatchery, A

This video features Maria, who talks about her trip to the Fish Hatchery to her classmates in a "show and tell" format. It shows the hatchery and the life cycle of the salmon, as Maria tells of her experiences on the tour.

Availability: Schools, libraries, homeschoolers, and nursing homes in the United States.
Suggested Grade: 4-8
Order Number: order by title
Format: VHS videotape
Special Notes: Closed captioned.
Terms: Borrower pays return postage. Return within 14 days after scheduled use, via UPS or Federal Express. Book at least 14 days in advance and include alternate date. Requests should include title(s), format, name of responsible person, organizational affiliation, phone, and complete delivery address. No part of any program can be used or duplicated without prior written permission. All programs are available for purchase at a nominal fee. May be available in other formats; inquire if interested. Online video previews are available.

Source: California Department of Water Resources
Attn: Video Library, Room 204-22
P. O. Box 942836
Sacramento, CA 94236-0001
Phone: 1-916-653-4893
Fax: 1-916-653-3310
World Wide Web URL: http://www.water.ca.gov/
Email Address: www.publicawillm@water.ca.gov

Webcytology: An Exploration of Unicellular Life

Comprehensive resource for learning about unicellular biology (cytology, the study of cells).

Availability: All requesters
Suggested Grade: 9-12
Order Number: not applicable
Format: Web Site
Special Notes: This URL will lead you to a subject page. Then click on the appropriate subject heading.

Source: ThinkQuest
World Wide Web URL:
http://www.thinkquest.org/pls/html/think.library

We Need Trees and Their Oxygen Cycle Lesson Plan

Students will examine plant photosynthesis and respiration and develop an understanding of where most of our oxygen comes from.

Availability: All requesters
Suggested Grade: 5
Order Number: not applicable
Format: Online Lesson Plan

Source: Patricia Wagner
World Wide Web URL:
http://sftrc.cas.psu.edu/LessonPlans/Forestry/WeNeed.html

What is a Seed?

Reveals how a seed is the beginning and end of a plant's life cycle; also some of the ways in which seeds are dispersed, and time-lapse germination sequences.

Availability: Schools, libraries, homeschoolers, and nursing homes in Illinois, Indiana, Iowa, Michigan, Minnesota, Missouri, Ohio, and Wisconsin only.
Suggested Grade: 9-12
Order Number: 347
Format: VHS videotape
Terms: Return postage is paid by borrower. Book 10-14 days in advance. Return 7 days after showing. Please provide alternate showing date.

Source: U. S. Fish and Wildlife Service
Region 3, Resource Library
3815 American Boulevard
Bloomington, MN 55425
Fax: 1-612-725-3279
Email Address: judy_geck@fws.gov

What's Inside Your Body? Bones & Muscles/Nervous System

Examines the bones, muscles, and nervous system of the human body.
Availability: Schools, libraries, and homeschoolers in the United States who serve the hearing impaired.
Suggested Grade: 2-6
Order Number: 12932
Production Date: 1999
Format: DVD
Terms: Sponsor pays all transportation costs. Return one week after receipt. Participation is limited to deaf or hard of hearing Americans, their parents, families, teachers, counselors, or others whose use would benefit a deaf or hard of hearing person. Only one person in the audience needs to be hearing impaired. You must register--which is free. These videos are all open-captioned--no special equipment is required for viewing.

Source: Described and Captioned Media Program
National Association of the Deaf
4211 Church Street Ext.
Roebuck, SC 29376
Phone: 1-800-237-6213
Fax: 1-800-538-5636
World Wide Web URL: http://www.dcmp.org

What's Inside Your Body? Heart & Blood/Digestion & Respiration

Young students discuss the heart, blood, makeup of the lungs, and the complex digestive system.
Availability: Schools, libraries, and homeschoolers in the United States who serve the hearing impaired.
Suggested Grade: 2-7
Order Number: 12933
Production Date: 1999
Format: DVD
Terms: Sponsor pays all transportation costs. Return one week after receipt. Participation is limited to deaf or hard of hearing Americans, their parents, families, teachers, counselors, or others whose use would benefit a deaf or hard of hearing person. Only one person in the audience needs to be hearing impaired. You must register--which is free. These videos are all open-captioned--no special equipment is required for viewing.

Source: Described and Captioned Media Program
National Association of the Deaf
4211 Church Street Ext.
Roebuck, SC 29376
Phone: 1-800-237-6213
Fax: 1-800-538-5636
World Wide Web URL: http://www.dcmp.org

Indicates an Internet Resource--just enter the URL and instantly access the FREE teaching aid you need!
All materials listed in this 2010-2011 edition are BRAND NEW!

77

NATURE STUDY

Alien Invasion of Hawaii!
Hawaii's plants and animals are under attack from foreign invaders--in this WebQuest you will look at how these visitors are causing the decline, and even extinction, of many native plant and animal species in Hawaii.

Availability: All requesters
Suggested Grade: 5-8
Order Number: not applicable
Format: WebQuest

Source: Karla Kingsley
World Wide Web URL: http://www.nevada.edu/~karla/

All About Farm Animals
Find out interesting facts about animals, play games, and take a quiz.

Availability: All requesters
Suggested Grade: K-3
Order Number: not applicable
Format: Web Site

Source: Kiddyhouse.com
World Wide Web URL: http://www.kiddyhouse.com/Farm/

Amphibian Embryology Tutorial
An online tutorial for learning more about amphibians.

Availability: All requesters
Suggested Grade: 10-Adult
Order Number: not applicable
Format: Online Tutorial

Source: Jeff Hardin
World Wide Web URL:
http://worms.zoology.wisc.edu/frogs/welcome.html

Amphibians and Reptiles of West Virginia
Lists various amphibians and reptiles found in West Virginia and their population status.

Availability: Classroom quantities to schools, libraries, and homeschoolers in the United States.
Suggested Grade: 3-12
Order Number: order by title
Format: Brochure

Source: West Virginia Wildlife Resources Section
West Virginia Division of Natural Resources
324 Fourth Avenue
South Charleston, WV 25303
Phone: 1-304-558-2771
Fax: 1-304-558-3147
World Wide Web URL: http://www.wvdnr.gov

Animaland
Here are games, contests, and lots of information on caring for pets.

Availability: All requesters
Suggested Grade: K-5
Order Number: not applicable
Format: Web Site

Source: American Society for the Prevention of Cruelty to Animals
World Wide Web URL: http://www.animaland.org/

Animal Behavior
Explores aspects of the biology and behavior of selected African mammals and birds.

Availability: All requesters
Suggested Grade: 5-12
Order Number: not applicable
Format: Web Site

Source: African Safari Holidays
World Wide Web URL:
http://www.wildlifeafrica.co.za/animalbehavior.html

Animal Communities and Groups
Presents a variety of animals that live together for mutual benefit in communities and groups. Illustrates the concept of "division of labor."

Availability: Schools, libraries, homeschoolers, and nursing homes in Illinois, Indiana, Iowa, Michigan, Minnesota, Missouri, Ohio, and Wisconsin only.
Suggested Grade: K-12
Order Number: 227
Format: VHS videotape
Terms: Return postage is paid by borrower. Book 10-14 days in advance. Return 7 days after showing. Please provide alternate showing date.

Source: U. S. Fish and Wildlife Service
Region 3, Resource Library
3815 American Boulevard
Bloomington, MN 55425
Fax: 1-612-725-3279
Email Address: judy_geck@fws.gov

Animal Info--Rare, Threatened and Endangered Mammals
Searchable information on rare, threatened and endangered mammals.

Availability: All requesters
Suggested Grade: 4-12
Order Number: not applicable
Format: Web Site

Source: Animal Info
World Wide Web URL: http://www.animalinfo.org/

Animals & Me Eating
What do chimpanzees, kodiak bears, and elephants eat? Three children explore the similarities and differences between themselves and animals and the foods they eat.

Availability: Schools, libraries, and homeschoolers in the United States who serve the hearing impaired.
Suggested Grade: 2-5
Order Number: 10815
Production Date: 1994
Format: DVD
Special Notes: Also available as live streaming video over the Internet.
Terms: Sponsor pays all transportation costs. Return one week after receipt. Participation is limited to deaf or hard of hearing Americans, their parents, families, teachers,

counselors, or others whose use would benefit a deaf or hard of hearing person. Only one person in the audience needs to be hearing impaired. You must register--which is free. These videos are all open-captioned--no special equipment is required for viewing.

Source: Described and Captioned Media Program
National Association of the Deaf
4211 Church Street Ext.
Roebuck, SC 29376
Phone: 1-800-237-6213
Fax: 1-800-538-5636
World Wide Web URL: http://www.dcmp.org

Animals and Their Homes
Introduction to various animal homes.

Availability: Schools, libraries, homeschoolers, and nursing homes in Illinois, Indiana, Iowa, Michigan, Minnesota, Missouri, Ohio, and Wisconsin only.
Suggested Grade: K-12
Order Number: 19
Format: VHS videotape
Terms: Return postage is paid by borrower. Book 10-14 days in advance. Return 7 days after showing. Please provide alternate showing date.

Source: U. S. Fish and Wildlife Service
Region 3, Resource Library
3815 American Boulevard
Bloomington, MN 55425
Fax: 1-612-725-3279
Email Address: judy_geck@fws.gov

Animals Concentration Game
Learn more about animals playing this matching game.

Availability: All requesters
Suggested Grade: 1-4
Platform: Macintosh; Windows
Order Number: not applicable
Format: Downloadable FULL PROGRAM

Source: School Express
World Wide Web URL:
http://www.schoolexpress.com/compsoft/software02.php

Animals of the Rainforest
Brings to life the signs and sounds of the rainforest.

Availability: Schools in the United States.
Suggested Grade: 3-6
Order Number: order by title
Format: VHS videotape
Terms: Borrower pays return postage. Return 14 days after receipt, via USPS including insurance. All borrowers must have a current lending agreement on file with the Outreach program. This agreement is available via the web site or may be requested via phone or fax.

Source: Center for Latin American Studies
University of Florida
319 Grinter Hall
P. O. Box 115530
Gainesville, FL 32611-5530

Phone: 1-352-392-0375
Fax: 1-352-392-7682
World Wide Web URL: http://www.latam.ufl.edu/outreach
Email Address: maryr@ufl.edu

Animals on the Ice Floe: Shiretoko in Mid-Winter
In winter, the sea along the Shiretoko peninsula in Hokkaido is surrounded with ice. This highlights some of the animals such as eagles and seals that live on the ice floe.

Availability: Schools, libraries and homeschoolers in Alabama, Georgia, North Carolina, South Carolina, and Virginia.
Suggested Grade: 4-Adult
Order Number: 511
Production Date: 1988
Format: VHS videotape
Special Notes: No. 11 of the "Document Japan" series.
Terms: Borrower pays return postage. Two tapes may be borrowed at a time. Return within 7 days after receipt. Reservations may be made by filling the application found on the web site.

Source: Consulate General of Japan, Atlanta
Japan Information Center
One Alliance Center
3500 Lenox Road, Suite 1600
Atlanta, GA 30326
Phone: 1-404-365-9240
Fax: 1-404-240-4311
World Wide Web URL:
http://www.atlanta.us.emb-japan.go.jp
Email Address: info@cgjapanatlanta.org

Animals on the Ice Floe: Shiretoko in Mid-Winter
In winter, the sea along the Shiretoko peninsula in Hokkaido is surrounded with ice. This highlights some of the animals such as eagles and seals that live on the ice floe.

Availability: Schools, libraries, homeschoolers, and nursing homes in Connecticut (except Fairfield County), Maine, Massachusetts, New Hampshire, Rhode Island, and Vermont.
Suggested Grade: 4-Adult
Order Number: 166
Production Date: 1988
Format: VHS videotape
Special Notes: No. 11 of the "Document Japan" series.
Terms: Borrower pays return postage, including insurance. Return two weeks after receipt.

Source: Consulate General of Japan, Boston
Federal Reserve Plaza, 14th Floor, 600 Atlantic Avenue
Boston, MA 02210
Phone: 1-617-973-9772
Fax: 1-617-542-1329
World Wide Web URL:
http://www.boston.us.emb-japan.go.jp
Email Address: infocul@cgjbos.org

Antlers Big and Small
Meet nearly a dozen different cousins of the deer family-from elk to deer.

Availability: Schools, libraries, homeschoolers, and nursing homes in Illinois, Indiana, Iowa, Michigan, Minnesota, Missouri, Ohio, and Wisconsin only.
Suggested Grade: K-12
Order Number: 284
Format: VHS videotape
Terms: Return postage is paid by borrower. Book 10-14 days in advance. Return 7 days after showing. Please provide alternate showing date.

Source: U. S. Fish and Wildlife Service
Region 3, Resource Library
3815 American Boulevard
Bloomington, MN 55425
Fax: 1-612-725-3279
Email Address: judy_geck@fws.gov

Arizona Bald Eagle Nest Watch Program

This award-winning documentary is about extremely rare desert-nesting bald eagles and the people who work to protect these magnificent birds. View up-close footage of wild bald eagles nesting and raising young in the extreme environments of the Arizona desert. By following teams of biologists and "nest watchers" you will also get personal views of the unique and successful Nest Watch Program. Learn what it is like to live outdoors and work with the majestic bald eagle.

Availability: Schools, libraries, homeschoolers, and nursing homes in Illinois, Indiana, Iowa, Michigan, Minnesota, Missouri, Ohio, and Wisconsin only.
Suggested Grade: 7-12
Order Number: 250
Format: VHS videotape
Terms: Return postage is paid by borrower. Book 10-14 days in advance. Return 7 days after showing. Please provide alternate showing date.

Source: U. S. Fish and Wildlife Service
Region 3, Resource Library
3815 American Boulevard
Bloomington, MN 55425
Fax: 1-612-725-3279
Email Address: judy_geck@fws.gov

Avibase

An extensive database information system about all birds of the world, containing over 2 million records about 10,000 species and 22,000 subspecies of birds.

Availability: All requesters
Suggested Grade: All ages
Order Number: not applicable
Format: Searchable Database
Source: Denis Lepage
World Wide Web URL:
http://www.bsc-eoc.org/avibase/avibase.jsp

Backyard Nature

All sorts of activities and ideas for learning about and celebrating nature in your own backyard.

Availability: All requesters
Suggested Grade: All ages
Order Number: not applicable
Format: Web Site
Source: Jim Conrad
World Wide Web URL: http://www.backyardnature.net/

Beavers and How They Live

Introduces beavers in their natural habitat. Shows beavers at work cutting trees and branches and building and repairing the lodge. Describes their physical features and behaviors. Explains their eating and sleeping habits and care for their young. Shows inside a lodge as beavers groom each other.

Availability: Schools, libraries, and homeschoolers in the United States who serve the hearing impaired.
Suggested Grade: 3-8
Order Number: 12357
Production Date: 1993
Format: DVD
Special Notes: Produced by Aims Multimedia.
Terms: Sponsor pays all transportation costs. Return one week after receipt. Participation is limited to deaf or hard of hearing Americans, their parents, families, teachers, counselors, or others whose use would benefit a deaf or hard of hearing person. Only one person in the audience needs to be hearing impaired. You must register--which is free. These videos are all open-captioned--no special equipment is required for viewing.

Source: Described and Captioned Media Program
National Association of the Deaf
4211 Church Street Ext.
Roebuck, SC 29376
Phone: 1-800-237-6213
Fax: 1-800-538-5636
World Wide Web URL: http://www.dcmp.org

Big Aquarium, The

Takes an armchair tour through the Tennessee Aquarium in Chattanooga and shows aquariums are a learning place from top to bottom.

Availability: Schools, libraries, and homeschoolers in the United States who serve the hearing impaired.
Suggested Grade: 2-5
Order Number: 11323
Production Date: 1998
Format: DVD
Special Notes: Also available as live streaming video over the Internet.
Terms: Sponsor pays all transportation costs. Return one week after receipt. Participation is limited to deaf or hard of hearing Americans, their parents, families, teachers, counselors, or others whose use would benefit a deaf or hard of hearing person. Only one person in the audience needs to be hearing impaired. You must register--which is free. These videos are all open-captioned--no special equipment is required for viewing.

Source: Described and Captioned Media Program
National Association of the Deaf
4211 Church Street Ext.
Roebuck, SC 29376
Phone: 1-800-237-6213
Fax: 1-800-538-5636
World Wide Web URL: http://www.dcmp.org

Big Green Caterpillar, The

Two elementary students find an egglike object on a leaf, and, with advice from their teacher, provide the right environment for it to grow. They watch as a caterpillar emerges.

Availability: Schools, libraries, and homeschoolers in the United States who serve the hearing impaired.
Suggested Grade: 2-5
Order Number: 13039
Production Date: 1994
Format: DVD
Terms: Sponsor pays all transportation costs. Return one week after receipt. Participation is limited to deaf or hard of hearing Americans, their parents, families, teachers, counselors, or others whose use would benefit a deaf or hard of hearing person. Only one person in the audience needs to be hearing impaired. You must register--which is free. These videos are all open-captioned--no special equipment is required for viewing.
Source: Described and Captioned Media Program
National Association of the Deaf
4211 Church Street Ext.
Roebuck, SC 29376
Phone: 1-800-237-6213
Fax: 1-800-538-5636
World Wide Web URL: http://www.dcmp.org

Birds of West Virginia

Lists the various birds found in West Virginia, their habitat preference, and their population status.

Availability: Classroom quantities to schools, libraries, and homeschoolers in the United States.
Suggested Grade: 3-12
Order Number: order by title
Format: Brochure
Source: West Virginia Wildlife Resources Section
West Virginia Division of Natural Resources
324 Fourth Avenue
South Charleston, WV 25303
Phone: 1-304-558-2771
Fax: 1-304-558-3147
World Wide Web URL: http://www.wvdnr.gov

Bluebird Quest, A

Find out more about bluebirds.
Availability: All requesters
Suggested Grade: All ages
Order Number: not applicable
Format: WebQuest

Source: Nancy Bocian, Christi Guptill, and Barbara Grollimund
World Wide Web URL:
http://www2.lhric.org/kat/BLUE.HTM

Breeds of Livestock

An educational and informational resource on breeds of livestock throughout the world.
Availability: All requesters
Suggested Grade: 6-12
Order Number: not applicable
Format: Web Site
Source: Department of Animal Science at Oklahoma State University
World Wide Web URL: http://www.ansi.okstate.edu/breeds/

Cetacean Fact Packs

Facts sheets about whales and dolphins.
Availability: All requesters
Suggested Grade: All ages
Order Number: not applicable
Format: Downloadable Fact Sheets
Source: American Cetacean Society
World Wide Web URL:
http://www.acsonline.org/factpack/index.html

Checklist of Kansas Dragonflies

Illustrates the many types of dragonflies found in Kansas and tells about their habits and habitat.
Availability: One copy to schools, libraries, and homeschoolers world-wide. May be copied.
Suggested Grade: 5-Adult
Order Number: Vol. 43, No. 2
Production Date: 1996
Format: Booklet
Special Notes: May also be downloaded from the web site.
Source: Kansas School Naturalist, The
Department of Biology, Box 4050
Emporia State University
Emporia, KS 66801-5087
Phone: 1-620-341-5614
Fax: 1-620-341-5607
World Wide Web URL:
www.emporia.edu/ksn/http://www.emporia.edu/ksn/
Email Address: ksnaturl@emporia.edu

Checklist of Kansas Jumping Spiders

Life cycle and habitat information about this fascinating, colorful hunting spider.
Availability: One copy to schools, libraries, and homeschoolers world-wide. May be copied.
Suggested Grade: 5-Adult
Order Number: Vol. 47, No. 1
Production Date: 2001
Format: Booklet
Special Notes: May also be downloaded from the web site.
Source: Kansas School Naturalist, The
Department of Biology, Box 4050, Emporia State University
Emporia, KS 66801-5087

 Indicates an Internet Resource--just enter the URL and instantly access the FREE teaching aid you need!
All materials listed in this 2010-2011 edition are BRAND NEW!

81

Phone: 1-620-341-5614
Fax: 1-620-341-5607
World Wide Web URL:
www.emporia.edu/ksn/http://www.emporia.edu/ksn/
Email Address: ksnaturl@emporia.edu

Climate Change and California
Discusses this topic.
Availability: One copy to schools, libraries, and homeschoolers world-wide.
Suggested Grade: 6-12
Order Number: 230F97008E
Format: Article
Source: U. S. Environmental Protection Agency, NSCEP
P. O. Box 42419
Cincinnati, OH 45242-2419
Phone: 1-800-490-9198
Fax: 1-301-604-3408
World Wide Web URL:
http://www.epa.gov/ncepihom/orderpub.html
Email Address: nscep@bps-lmit.com

Climate Change and Illinois
Discusses this topic.
Availability: One copy to schools, libraries, and homeschoolers world-wide.
Suggested Grade: 6-12
Order Number: 230F97008M
Format: Article
Source: U. S. Environmental Protection Agency, NSCEP
P. O. Box 42419
Cincinnati, OH 45242-2419
Phone: 1-800-490-9198
Fax: 1-301-604-3408
World Wide Web URL:
http://www.epa.gov/ncepihom/orderpub.html
Email Address: nscep@bps-lmit.com

Climate Change and New Hampshire
Discusses this topic.
Availability: One copy to schools, libraries, and homeschoolers world-wide.
Suggested Grade: 6-12
Order Number: 230F97008CC
Format: Article
Source: U. S. Environmental Protection Agency, NSCEP
P. O. Box 42419
Cincinnati, OH 45242-2419
Phone: 1-800-490-9198
Fax: 1-301-604-3408
World Wide Web URL:
http://www.epa.gov/ncepihom/orderpub.html
Email Address: nscep@bps-lmit.com

Climate Change and New Jersey
Discusses this topic.
Availability: One copy to schools, libraries, and homeschoolers world-wide.
Suggested Grade: 6-12

Order Number: 230F97008DD
Format: Article
Source: U. S. Environmental Protection Agency, NSCEP
P. O. Box 42419
Cincinnati, OH 45242-2419
Phone: 1-800-490-9198
Fax: 1-301-604-3408
World Wide Web URL:
http://www.epa.gov/ncepihom/orderpub.html
Email Address: nscep@bps-lmit.com

Climate Change and New Mexico
Discusses this topic.
Availability: One copy to schools, libraries, and homeschoolers world-wide.
Suggested Grade: 6-12
Order Number: 236F98007P
Format: Article
Source: U. S. Environmental Protection Agency, NSCEP
P. O. Box 42419
Cincinnati, OH 45242-2419
Phone: 1-800-490-9198
Fax: 1-301-604-3408
World Wide Web URL:
http://www.epa.gov/ncepihom/orderpub.html
Email Address: nscep@bps-lmit.com

Climate Change and New York
Discusses this topic.
Availability: One copy to schools, libraries, and homeschoolers world-wide.
Suggested Grade: 6-12
Order Number: 230F97008FF
Format: Article
Source: U. S. Environmental Protection Agency, NSCEP
P. O. Box 42419
Cincinnati, OH 45242-2419
Phone: 1-800-490-9198
Fax: 1-301-604-3408
World Wide Web URL:
http://www.epa.gov/ncepihom/orderpub.html
Email Address: nscep@bps-lmit.com

Climate Change and Wisconsin
Discusses this topic.
Availability: One copy to schools, libraries, and homeschoolers world-wide.
Suggested Grade: 6-12
Order Number: 230F97008WW
Format: Article
Source: U. S. Environmental Protection Agency, NSCEP
P. O. Box 42419
Cincinnati, OH 45242-2419
Phone: 1-800-490-9198
Fax: 1-301-604-3408
World Wide Web URL:
http://www.epa.gov/ncepihom/orderpub.html
Email Address: nscep@bps-lmit.com

Indicates an Internet Resource--just enter the URL and instantly access the FREE teaching aid you need!
*All materials listed in this 2010-2011 edition are **BRAND NEW!***

Collection and Maintenance of Ants and Studying Ants

Shows how to collect and maintain ants with the minimum amount of work and expense.

Availability: One copy to schools, libraries, and homeschoolers world-wide. May be copied.
Suggested Grade: 5-Adult
Order Number: Volume 41, No. 1
Production Date: 1994
Format: Booklet
Special Notes: May also be downloaded from the web site.

Source: Kansas School Naturalist, The
Department of Biology, Box 4050
Emporia State University
Emporia, KS 66801-5087
Phone: 1-620-341-5614
Fax: 1-620-341-5607
World Wide Web URL:
www.emporia.edu/ksn/http://www.emporia.edu/ksn/
Email Address: ksnaturl@emporia.edu

Design a Greenhouse

Your new job as a greenhouse manager requires you to learn more about plant survival.

Availability: All requesters
Suggested Grade: 9-12
Order Number: not applicable
Format: WebQuest

Source: Donna Chaney, Dawn Davis, and Melissa Garber
World Wide Web URL:
http://www.milforded.org/schools/foran/
mgarber/wq/greenhouse.html

Disguise and Camouflage in Tropical Insects

See how tropical insects have evolved a variety of means of hiding from their predators.

Availability: Schools and libraries in Iowa, Illinois, Michigan, Minnesota, and Wisconsin.
Suggested Grade: 4-12
Order Number: ENVLAD63SLIDES
Format: Set of 10 slides
Special Notes: Includes a script.
Terms: Borrower pays return postage. Return 8 days after showing. Book 2 weeks in advance. Order may also be picked up for those near the Center.

Source: Center for Latin American and Caribbean Studies
UW-Milwaukee
P. O. Box 413
Milwaukee, WI 53201
Phone: 1-414-229-5987
World Wide Web URL: http://www.uwm.edu/Dept/CLACS
Email Address: audvis@usm.edu

Do Animals Play Hide and Seek?

Helps youngsters answer this question.

Availability: All requesters
Suggested Grade: K
Order Number: not applicable
Format: Online Lesson Plan

Source: Kelly Smith
World Wide Web URL:
http://www.eduref.org/Virtual/Lessons/Science/
Animals/ANM0114.html

Dolphin-Safe Tuna?

Explores this issue.

Availability: All requesters
Suggested Grade: 4-12
Order Number: not applicable
Format: WebQuest

Source: Melissa Buray, Robin Fleet, and Cynthia Rieker
World Wide Web URL:
http://oncampus.richmond.edu/academics/education/
projects/webquests/dolphins/

Economics of Wetlands, The

An online course to help students develop a better understanding of wetlands.

Availability: All requesters
Suggested Grade: 7-Adult
Order Number: not applicable
Format: Online Course

Source: Kenilworth Park and Aquatic Gardens
World Wide Web URL:
http://www.nps.gov/keaq/forteachers

Ecosystems

Students will learn more about biodiversity and ecosystems as they visit a small part of the school grounds, a local park, or even a National Park.

Availability: All requesters
Suggested Grade: 6-8
Order Number: not applicable
Format: Online Lesson Plan

Source: R. Mark Herzog
World Wide Web URL:
http://school.discovery.com/lessonplans/programs/yosemite/

Education Fact Sheets

Downloadable fact sheets about all sorts of animals usually found in aquariums as well as career information.

Availability: All requesters
Suggested Grade: 4-12
Order Number: not applicable
Format: Online Articles

Source: National Aquarium in Baltimore
World Wide Web URL:
http://www.aqua.org/educators_factsheets.html

Elasmobranch Fisheries Management Techniques

A complete manual that provides the basic information to manage shark fisheries. Great for advanced research projects on sharks and other such mammals.

Availability: All requesters
Suggested Grade: 9-Adult
Order Number: not applicable
Format: Online Manual

 Indicates an Internet Resource--just enter the URL and instantly access the FREE teaching aid you need!
*All materials listed in this 2010-2011 edition are **BRAND NEW!***

83

Source: Florida Museum of Natural History Ichthyology
Department
World Wide Web URL:
http://www.flmnh.ufl.edu/fish/organizations/ssg/
EFMT2004.htm

Electronic Zoo, The

Provides information about thousands of animals.

Availability: All requesters
Suggested Grade: All ages
Order Number: not applicable
Format: Web Site
Source: Ken Boschert, DVM
World Wide Web URL: http://netvet.wustl.edu/e-zoo.htm

Elephant Information Repository

An in-depth resource for elephant related news, events, and a "trunk" full of elephant related information.

Availability: All requesters
Suggested Grade: 6-12
Order Number: not applicable
Format: Web Site
Source: Paul MacKenzie
World Wide Web URL: http://elephant.elehost.com/

Emas Park

Examines animal and plant life found in this national park in the high plains of Brazil.

Availability: Schools, libraries, and nursing homes in the United States.
Suggested Grade: 6-12
Order Number: GEBRA4-video
Production Date: 1985
Format: VHS videotape
Terms: Borrowers must have a User's Agreement on file with this source--available by mail or via the Internet. Return postage is paid by borrower; return 12 days after showing. Book at least three weeks in advance. All borrowers are limited to a total of ten items per semester.
Source: Latin American Resource Center
Stone Center for Latin American Studies
Tulane University
100 Jones Hall
New Orleans, LA 70118
Phone: 1-504-862-3143
Fax: 1-504-865-6719
World Wide Web URL:
http://stonecenter.tulane.edu/LARCLLCatalogue.htm
Email Address: crcrts@tulane.edu

Endangered Species

Dedicated to providing information about endangered species as well as information on conservation efforts.

Availability: All requesters
Suggested Grade: 4-12
Order Number: not applicable
Format: Web Site
Source: Lauren Kurpis
World Wide Web URL: http://www.endangeredspecie.com/

Exploring the Parts of a Plant

After students learn about the 6 basic plant parts, they will create a game or activity so that others may learn the same thing.

Availability: All requesters
Suggested Grade: 4-8
Order Number: not applicable
Format: WebQuest
Source: Colleen Boyea
World Wide Web URL:
http://its.guilford.k12.nc.us/webquests/plantquest/

Extreme Cave Diving

A team of intrepid scientists journey into one of Earth's most dangerous and beautiful underwater frontiers.

Availability: All requesters
Suggested Grade: 7-Adult
Order Number: not applicable
Production Date: 2010
Format: Streaming Video
Source: NOVA
World Wide Web URL:
http://www.pbs.org/wgbh/nova/programs/index.html

Farm Animals

Helps kids learn about farm life when they don't have access to one.

Availability: All requesters
Suggested Grade: preK-4
Order Number: not applicable
Format: Web Site
Source: Red Bluff Ranch
World Wide Web URL: http://www.kidsfarm.com/farm.htm

Feral Pigeons

Information about the life and habitat of these birds.

Availability: One copy to schools, libraries, and homeschoolers world-wide. May be copied.
Suggested Grade: 5-Adult
Order Number: Volume 45, No. 2
Production Date: 1998
Format: Booklet
Special Notes: May also be downloaded from the web site.
Source: Kansas School Naturalist, The
Department of Biology, Box 4050
Emporia State University
Emporia, KS 66801-5087
Phone: 1-620-341-5614
Fax: 1-620-341-5607
World Wide Web URL:
www.emporia.edu/ksn/http://www.emporia.edu/ksn/
Email Address: ksnaturl@emporia.edu

Field Trip Earth

Take your students on a world tour as they learn about Appalachian black bears, red wolves of Alligator River, the elephants of Cameroon and many more species without ever leaving the classroom.

Availability: All requesters
Suggested Grade: All ages
Order Number: not applicable
Format: Web Site
Source: North Carolina Zoological Society
World Wide Web URL: http://www.fieldtripearth.org/

Fishes of West Virginia
A checklist of the presently known species of fish in West Virginia.
Availability: Classroom quantities to schools, libraries, and homeschoolers in the United States.
Suggested Grade: 3-12
Order Number: order by title
Format: Brochure
Source: West Virginia Wildlife Resources Section
West Virginia Division of Natural Resources
324 Fourth Avenue
South Charleston, WV 25303
Phone: 1-304-558-2771
Fax: 1-304-558-3147
World Wide Web URL: http://www.wvdnr.gov

Florida Panther Net
A complete web site devoted to teaching students about the state animal of Florida. Includes games, activities, lesson plans, and more.
Availability: All requesters
Suggested Grade: All ages
Order Number: not applicable
Format: Web Site
Source: Florida Panther Net
World Wide Web URL:
http://www.panther.state.fl.us/index.html

Friends of the Sea Otter Information--High School
Lots of information about this mammal.
Availability: All requesters
Suggested Grade: 9-12
Order Number: not applicable
Format: Downloadable Materials
Special Notes: This is a PDF file which will open automatically on your computer.
Source: Friends of the Sea Otter
World Wide Web URL: http://www.seaotters.org/pdfs/
highschoolmaterial.pdf?DocID=340

Friends of the Sea Otter Information--Middle
Lots of information about this mammal.
Availability: All requesters
Suggested Grade: 5-8
Order Number: not applicable
Format: Downloadable Materials
Special Notes: This is a PDF file which will open automatically on your computer.
Source: Friends of the Sea Otter
World Wide Web URL:
http://www.seaotters.org/pdfs/middleschoolmaterials.pdf

Friends of the Sea Otter Information--Elementary
Lots of information about this mammal.
Availability: All requesters
Suggested Grade: 1-4
Order Number: not applicable
Format: Downloadable Materials
Special Notes: This is a PDF file which will open automatically on your computer.
Source: Friends of the Sea Otter (elem)
World Wide Web URL:
http://www.seaotters.org/pdfs/elementarymaterials.pdf

Froggy Page, The
Information about frogs from literature to science.
Availability: All requesters
Suggested Grade: All ages
Order Number: not applicable
Format: Web Site
Source: Sandra Loosemore
World Wide Web URL: http://www.frogsonice.com/froggy/

Frogland
Includes frog facts, frogs in the news, frog jokes and much more.
Availability: All requesters
Suggested Grade: All ages
Order Number: not applicable
Format: Web Site
Source: Dorota
World Wide Web URL:
http://allaboutfrogs.org/froglnd.shtml

From Whaling to Watching: The Northern Right Whale
Shows spectacular footage of these rare whales and helps us realize the role we all have to play in protecting the most endangered of the large whales.
Availability: Schools, libraries, and homeschoolers in Connecticut, Maine, Massachusetts, New Hampshire, Rhode Island, and Vermont.
Suggested Grade: 6-12
Order Number: VID 299
Production Date: 1997
Format: VHS videotape
Terms: Borrower pays return postage. Return within three weeks of receipt. If the tape you request is available, it will be mailed within 5 business days. If not, you will be notified that this video is already out on loan. No more than three titles may be borrowed by one requestor at a time. No reservations for a specific date will be accepted. It is most efficient to order via the web site.
Source: U. S. Environmental Protection Agency, Region 1
Customer Service Center
One Congress Street, Suite 1100
Boston, MA 02214
World Wide Web URL:
http://yosemite.epa.gov/r1/videolen.nsf/

 Indicates an Internet Resource--just enter the URL and instantly access the FREE teaching aid you need!
*All materials listed in this 2010-2011 edition are **BRAND NEW!***

85

Gaining Ground for Wildlife: North American Waterfowl Management Plan

This video shows the importance of continental involvement due to the migratory nature of waterfowl. Seven joint ventures are shown.

Availability: Schools, libraries, homeschoolers, and nursing homes in Illinois, Indiana, Iowa, Michigan, Minnesota, Missouri, Ohio, and Wisconsin only.
Suggested Grade: 9-12
Order Number: 418
Format: VHS videotape
Terms: Return postage is paid by borrower. Book 10-14 days in advance. Return 7 days after showing. Please provide alternate showing date.

Source: U. S. Fish and Wildlife Service
Region 3, Resource Library
3815 American Boulevard
Bloomington, MN 55425
Fax: 1-612-725-3279
World Wide Web URL:
Email Address: judy_geck@fws.gov

Galapagos: Beyond Darwin

Charles Darwin's historic voyage to the Galapagos Islands forever changed our view of the world, but he only scratched the surface. Climb into a state-of-the-art submersible and plunge 3,000 feet beneath the surface as history's first deep-diving expedition to the Galapagos probes where no camera has gone before.

Availability: Schools and libraries in Iowa, Illinois, Michigan, Minnesota, and Wisconsin.
Suggested Grade: 6-12
Order Number: ENVECUG13.1VHS
Production Date: 1996
Format: VHS videotape
Terms: Borrower pays return postage. Return 8 days after showing. Book 2 weeks in advance. Order may also be picked up for those near the Center.

Source: Center for Latin American and Caribbean Studies
UW-Milwaukee
P. O. Box 413
Milwaukee, WI 53201
Phone: 1-414-229-5987
World Wide Web URL: http://www.uwm.edu/Dept/CLACS
Email Address: audvis@usm.edu

Get Ready, Get Set, Grow!

The Brooklyn Children's Garden, where generations of children have gotten dirt under their fingernails, introduces students to the wonders of plant growth, and the basics of gardening, engendering respect for the natural world. After all, "Only plants can make food!"

Availability: Schools, libraries, homeschoolers, and nursing homes in the United States.
Suggested Grade: 1-8
Order Number: order by title
Production Date: 1986

Format: VHS videotape
Special Notes: Accompanied by information for children and adults on how to start a community garden.
Terms: Borrower pays return postage. Return the day after scheduled showing, via UPS or Priority Mail, insured for $100.00. Book 4 weeks in advance and include an alternate date. Order should include name of person responsible for handling the video, and complete mailing address. Please mention this Guide when ordering. Tapes may not be duplicated, edited or exhibited for a fee.

Source: Church World Service
Film & Video Library
28606 Phillips Street, P. O. Box 968
Elkhart, IN 46515
Phone: 1-800-297-1516, ext. 338
Fax: 1-574-262-0966
World Wide Web URL: http://www.churchworldservice.org
Email Address: videos@churchworldservice.org

Greater Prairie Chicken

Information about the life and habitat of this animal.

Availability: One copy to schools, libraries, and homeschoolers world-wide. May be copied.
Suggested Grade: 5-Adult
Order Number: Volume 45, No. 1
Production Date: 1998
Format: Booklet
Special Notes: May also be downloaded from the web site.

Source: Kansas School Naturalist, The
Department of Biology, Box 4050
Emporia State University
Emporia, KS 66801-5087
Phone: 1-620-341-5614
Fax: 1-620-341-5607
World Wide Web URL:
www.emporia.edu/ksn/http://www.emporia.edu/ksn/
Email Address: ksnaturl@emporia.edu

Growing Native

Allows students to explore native plant communities and the invasive species that compete with native plants.

Availability: All requesters
Suggested Grade: 6-8
Order Number: not applicable
Format: Online Lesson Plan

Source: Wildlife Habitat Council
World Wide Web URL:
http://www.wildlifehc.org/managementtools/
backyard-lessonplans.cfm

Hoptoad Habitats

Guides students through an exploration of amphibian habitats with a focus on vernal pools.

Availability: All requesters
Suggested Grade: 3-5
Order Number: not applicable
Format: Online Lesson Plan

Source: Wildlife Habitat Council
World Wide Web URL:
http://www.wildlifehc.org/managementtools/
backyard-lessonplans.cfm

Investigating Insects
Your task is to learn about the important role that insects play in our everyday lives. You will be able to identify insects and know whether they are beneficial or not.
Availability: All requesters
Suggested Grade: 8-12
Order Number: not applicable
Format: WebQuest
Source: Ashley Noblitt
World Wide Web URL:
http://www.mofb.org/webquest/wq46a.htm

Investigating Plants
Find the answers to these many questions about plants, by visiting listed web sites.
Availability: All requesters
Suggested Grade: 4
Order Number: not applicable
Format: WebQuest
Source: Gerald Robillard and Dee Charbonneau
World Wide Web URL:
http://www.swlauriersb.qc.ca/english/edservices/
pedresources/webquest/plants.htm

Is It a White Bass or a White Perch?
Tips on how to distinguish between these two species, one a native and the other an exotic.
Availability: Single copies to schools, libraries, and homeschoolers world-wide. May be copied for classroom distribution.
Suggested Grade: 4-12
Order Number: FS-005
Format: Fact Sheet
Special Notes: May also be downloaded from the web site.
Source: Ohio Sea Grant Publications
Attn: Nancy Cruickshank
1314 Kinnear Road
Columbus, OH 43212-1194
Phone: 1-614-292-8949
Fax: 1-614-292-4364
World Wide Web URL:
http://www.ohioseagrant.osu.edu/publications/

Katerpillars (& Mystery Bugs)
A good site for learning all about insects.
Availability: All requesters
Suggested Grade: K-4
Order Number: not applicable
Format: Web Site
Source: Pat Dillon
World Wide Web URL:
http://www.uky.edu/Agriculture/Entomology/
ythfacts/oldentyouth.htm

Kentucky Bug Connection Teaching Resources
Entomology resources for parents and educators.
Availability: All requesters
Suggested Grade: 6-12
Order Number: not applicable
Format: Online Lesson Plans and Curriculum Guides
Source: University of Kentucky Entomology
World Wide Web URL:
http://www.uky.edu/Agriculture/CritterFiles/casefile/
bugconnection/teaching/teaching.htm

KidsPlanet
Here are facts sheets on more than 50 species of wildlife, presented to help students understand how they can defend wildlife and help protect their environment.
Availability: All requesters
Suggested Grade: 3-8
Order Number: not applicable
Format: Web Site
Source: Defenders of Wildlife
World Wide Web URL: http://www.kidsplanet.org

Kratt's Creatures: Arribada 1: The Sea Turtle Invasion/Arribada 2: Running the Gauntlet
In Costa Rica, once a year the "Arribada" happens: hundreds of thousands of sea turtles simultaneously swim ashore to lay their eggs on the beach. This video shows more of this amazing process.
Availability: Schools and libraries in Iowa, Illinois, Michigan, Minnesota, and Wisconsin.
Suggested Grade: 4-12
Order Number: ENVCRK86.1VHS
Production Date: 1996
Format: VHS videotape
Special Notes: Shown in two segments of 30 minutes each.
Terms: Borrower pays return postage. Return 8 days after showing. Book 2 weeks in advance. Order may also be picked up for those near the Center.
Source: Center for Latin American and Caribbean Studies
UW-Milwaukee
P. O. Box 413
Milwaukee, WI 53201
Phone: 1-414-229-5987
World Wide Web URL: http://www.uwm.edu/Dept/CLACS
Email Address: audvis@usm.edu

Kratt's Creatures: Creatures of the Night and Hanging with the Monkeys
Learn more about the different species of rainforest monkeys in Costa Rica.
Availability: Schools and libraries in Iowa, Illinois, Michigan, Minnesota, and Wisconsin.
Suggested Grade: 4-12
Order Number: ENVCRK86.2VHS
Production Date: 1996
Format: VHS videotape

 Indicates an Internet Resource--just enter the URL and instantly access the FREE teaching aid you need!
All materials listed in this 2010-2011 edition are BRAND NEW!

87

Special Notes: Shown in two segments of 30 minutes each.

Terms: Borrower pays return postage. Return 8 days after showing. Book 2 weeks in advance. Order may also be picked up for those near the Center.

Source: Center for Latin American and Caribbean Studies
UW-Milwaukee
P. O. Box 413
Milwaukee, WI 53201
Phone: 1-414-229-5987
World Wide Web URL: http://www.uwm.edu/Dept/CLACS
Email Address: audvis@usm.edu

Lesson 10: The Fascinating World of Insects--A Lesson in Bug Making with Friendly Clay

Provides an exciting interdisciplinary study of insects, including art, science, history, and writing.

Availability: Limit of 12 copies to schools, libraries, and homeschoolers in the United States and Canada.

Suggested Grade: K-9

Order Number: 30101C

Format: Lesson Plan

Special Notes: May also be downloaded from the web site.

Source: American Art Clay Co., Inc.
Sales Support
6060 Guion Road
Indianapolis, IN 46254
Phone: 1-800-374-1600
Fax: 1-317-248-9300
World Wide Web URL: http://www.amaco.com
Email Address: salessupport@amaco.com

Lewis and Clark as Naturalists

Learn about the plants and animals Lewis and Clark found along their great journey.

Availability: All requesters

Suggested Grade: 3-8

Order Number: not applicable

Format: Web Site

Source: Smithsonian National Museum of Natural History
World Wide Web URL:
http://www.mnh.si.edu/lewisandclark/
index.html?loc=/lewisandclark/home.html

Lizard Kings

Meet the monitors, the largest, fiercest and craftiest lizards on Earth.

Availability: All requesters

Suggested Grade: 7-Adult

Order Number: not applicable

Production Date: 2009

Format: Streaming Video

Source: NOVA
World Wide Web URL:
http://www.pbs.org/wgbh/nova/programs/index.html

Mammals and Birds

Students will learn the distinguishing characteristics between mammals and birds.

Availability: All requesters

Suggested Grade: 3

Order Number: not applicable

Format: Online Lesson Plan

Source: Rachelle Hrabosky
World Wide Web URL:
http://www.eduref.org/Virtual/Lessons/Science/
Animals/ANM0209.html

Manatees & Dugongs

A wonderful book about these mammals--when printed each illustration is suitable for coloring.

Availability: All requesters

Suggested Grade: 2-8

Order Number: not applicable

Format: Online Book

Source: Kerrie Kuzmier and Jennifer McCann
World Wide Web URL:
http://www.cep.unep.org/kids/kids.html

Mealworm Project

Students perform various experiments and observe the life cycle of mealworms they raise on their own.

Availability: All requesters

Suggested Grade: 5-12

Order Number: not applicable

Format: Online Lesson Plan

Source: Carrie Flores
World Wide Web URL:
http://teachertech.rice.edu/Participants/
cflores/lessons/mealworm/index.html

Melissa Kaplan's Herp Care Information Collection

Everything you want to know about raising reptiles as pets-- includes a section on convincing parents you can take care of one and that they are really cool pets.

Availability: All requesters

Suggested Grade: All ages

Order Number: not applicable

Format: Web Site

Source: Melissa Kaplan
World Wide Web URL: http://www.anapsid.org/

MendelWeb

Information on the genetics of plants.

Availability: All requesters

Suggested Grade: 9-12

Order Number: not applicable

Format: Web Site

Source: Roger B. Blumberg
World Wide Web URL: http://www.mendelweb.org/

Monarch Watch

Information about these beautiful butterflies as well as lesson plans.

Availability: All requesters

Suggested Grade: K-12

Order Number: not applicable
Format: Web Site
Source: University of Kansas Entomology Program
World Wide Web URL: http://www.monarchwatch.org/

Monterey Bay Aquarium Home Page
Here you will find 5 live cams that will allow you to watch the animals in the aquarium as if you were there.

Availability: All requesters
Suggested Grade: All ages
Order Number: not applicable
Format: Web Site
Source: Monterey Bay Aquarium
World Wide Web URL: http://www.mbayaq.org/

Most Wanted Bugs
A fun site to help children learn about insects.
Availability: All requesters
Suggested Grade: K-5
Order Number: not applicable
Format: Web Site
Source: Dennis Kunkel
World Wide Web URL:
http://education.denniskunkel.com/index.php

Nature Activities
Get involved online through videos, quizzes, eCards, and more and learn something new about the world around us.
Availability: All requesters
Suggested Grade: All ages
Order Number: not applicable
Format: Web Site
Source: Nature Conservancy, The
World Wide Web URL: http://nature.org/activities/

Nature's Glory: The Beauty of Taiwan
Ranging in climate from tropical to alpine in just 23,000 square miles, Taiwan houses a rich natural ecosystem, including a rare coral reef and unspoiled rain forest. This video introduces four national parks that have been established since 1977, highlighting special geological features and rare animal and plant species.
Availability: Schools, libraries, and nursing homes in the United States and Canada.
Suggested Grade: All ages
Order Number: TV006
Format: VHS videotape
Terms: Borrower pays return postage. Return with 14 days after scheduled showing, via UPS or U. S. Mail. All requests must included an educational institution affiliation, a current address, and phone number. Order through web site only.
Source: Cornell University East Asia Program
World Wide Web URL:
http://www.einaudi.cornell.edu/eastasia/outreach/video.asp
Email Address: east_asia1@cornell.edu

Neotropical Birds of West Virginia
Lists birds which breed in West Virginia but migrate to the tropics each winter.
Availability: Limit of 5 copies to schools, libraries, and homeschoolers in the United States.
Suggested Grade: 3-12
Order Number: order by title
Format: Brochure
Source: West Virginia Wildlife Resources Section
West Virginia Division of Natural Resources
324 Fourth Avenue
South Charleston, WV 25303
Phone: 1-304-558-2771
Fax: 1-304-558-3147
World Wide Web URL: http://www.wvdnr.gov

New Zealand Brown Teal Online
Provides information about this critically endangered duck and the efforts to help conserve and manage them.
Availability: All requesters
Suggested Grade: All ages
Order Number: not applicable
Format: Web Site
Source: brownteal.com
World Wide Web URL: http://www.brownteal.com/

Nonindigenous Species: Activities for Youth
A detailed manual of activities for helping students to learn about exotic species of plants and animals.
Availability: All requesters
Suggested Grade: 2-8
Order Number: not applicable
Format: Downloadable Book; 55 pages
Source: John Guyton, Dave Burrage and Rick Kastner
World Wide Web URL:
http://msstate.edu/dept/crec/nis.html

Owl Pellets
As students dissect an owl pellet, this lesson will help them learn more about the food chain as well as skeletal parts of animals ingested by owls.
Availability: All requesters
Suggested Grade: 4-12
Order Number: not applicable
Format: Online Lesson Plan
Source: Jeanette Vratil
World Wide Web URL:
http://www.eduref.org/Virtual/Lessons/Science/
Animals/ANM0045.html

Penguin World
Penguins are observed in their natural habitats hunting, mating, brooding, and raising their young.
Availability: Schools, libraries, homeschoolers, and nursing homes in Illinois, Indiana, Iowa, Michigan, Minnesota, Missouri, Ohio, and Wisconsin only.
Suggested Grade: 6-12

Order Number: 222
Production Date: 1992
Format: VHS videotape
Terms: Return postage is paid by borrower. Book 10-14 days in advance. Return 7 days after showing. Please provide alternate showing date.

Source: U. S. Fish and Wildlife Service
Region 3, Resource Library
3815 American Boulevard
Bloomington, MN 55425
Fax: 1-612-725-3279
World Wide Web URL:
Email Address: judy_geck@fws.gov

Peregrine Falcons in Acadia

Here is the story of this endangered species and the reintroduction of these birds to Acadia National Park.
Availability: Limit of 5 copies to schools, libraries, and homeschoolers world-wide.
Suggested Grade: K-12
Order Number: order by title
Production Date: 2008
Format: Brochure

Source: Acadia National Park
Information
P. O. Box 177
Bar Harbor, ME 04609
Phone: 1-207-288-3338
Fax: 1-207-288-8813
World Wide Web URL: http://www.nps.gov/acad
Email Address: acadia_information@nps.gov

Permian Insect Fossils of Elmo, Kansas, The

Discusses the variety, quantity, and quality of insect fossils found in the Kansas Permian limestone.
Availability: One copy to schools, libraries, and homeschoolers world-wide. May be copied.
Suggested Grade: 5-Adult
Order Number: Vol. 46, No. 1
Production Date: 2000
Format: Article
Special Notes: May also be downloaded from the web site.

Source: Kansas School Naturalist, The
Department of Biology, Box 4050
Emporia State University
Emporia, KS 66801-5087
Phone: 1-620-341-5614
Fax: 1-620-341-5607
World Wide Web URL:
www.emporia.edu/ksn/http://www.emporia.edu/ksn/
Email Address: ksnaturl@emporia.edu

Pioneer Virtual Zoo

Information about 182 different species--a real virtual zoo.
Availability: All requesters
Suggested Grade: All ages
Order Number: not applicable
Format: Web Site

Source: Pioneer Middle School
World Wide Web URL:
http://pioneerunion.ca.schoolwebpages.com/education/staff/
staff.php?sectionid=146&sc_id=1162170277

Plants

Written to develop an understanding of the many types of plants and their characteristics.
Availability: All requesters
Suggested Grade: 4-10
Order Number: not applicable
Format: Online Lesson Plans

Source: Dr. Alex C. Pan
World Wide Web URL: http://pan.tcnj.edu/plant.htm

Plants of the Rain Forest

Introduces students to some of the many flowers, vines, fungi and tees found from the forest floor to the top of the forest canopy. Filmed in the rainforests of Costa Rica.
Availability: Schools in the United States.
Suggested Grade: 3-6
Order Number: order by title
Format: VHS videotape
Terms: Borrower pays return postage. Return 14 days after receipt, via USPS including insurance. All borrowers must have a current lending agreement on file with the Outreach program. This agreement is available via the web site or may be requested via phone or fax.

Source: Center for Latin American Studies
University of Florida
319 Grinter Hall
P. O. Box 115530
Gainesville, FL 32611-5530
Phone: 1-352-392-0375
Fax: 1-352-392-7682
World Wide Web URL: http://www.latam.ufl.edu/outreach
Email Address: maryr@ufl.edu

Polar Bear Fact and Opinion WebQuest

This webquest will lead you on a journey to the home of the Polar Bear and discover facts. Includes a live Polar Bear Cam.
Availability: All requesters
Suggested Grade: 2-8
Order Number: not applicable
Format: WebQuest

Source: V. S. Bell
World Wide Web URL:
http://edujourney.net/Webquests/PolarBear/PolarBear.htm

POP Goes Antarctica?

Follow this teacher as she joins a team of scientists to research the effects of persistent organic pollutants on the food web of Antarctica.
Availability: All requesters
Suggested Grade: 6-12
Order Number: not applicable
Format: Web Site

Source: Susan Cowles
World Wide Web URL:
http://literacynet.org/polar/pop/html/project.html

Prairie Fires

Discusses the history of prairie fires in Kansas and explains why they benefit wildlife.

Availability: Classroom quantities to schools, libraries, and homeschoolers world-wide. May be copied.
Suggested Grade: 5-Adult
Order Number: Vol. 39, No. 2
Production Date: 1993
Format: Article
Special Notes: May also be downloaded from the web site.

Source: Kansas School Naturalist, The
Department of Biology, Box 4050
Emporia State University
Emporia, KS 66801-5087
Phone: 1-620-341-5614
Fax: 1-620-341-5607
World Wide Web URL:
www.emporia.edu/ksn/http://www.emporia.edu/ksn/
Email Address: ksnaturl@emporia.edu

Prisoners or Protected?

Explores whether zoos are considered humane environments or more like prisons.

Availability: All requesters
Suggested Grade: 5
Order Number: not applicable
Format: WebQuest

Source: Beverly Connolly, Maggie Gordon, and Cathy
Shulof
World Wide Web URL:
http://oncampus.richmond.edu/academics/education/
projects/webquests/zoos/

Rain Forest

Journey to the dense rain forests of Costa Rica and watch as leaf-cutting ants carry sections of leaves many times their weight to underground fungus gardens.

Availability: Schools in the United States.
Suggested Grade: All ages
Order Number: order by title
Format: VHS videotape
Terms: Borrower pays return postage. Return 14 days after receipt, via USPS including insurance. All borrowers must have a current lending agreement on file with the Outreach program. This agreement is available via the web site or may be requested via phone or fax.

Source: Center for Latin American Studies
University of Florida
319 Grinter Hall
P. O. Box 115530
Gainesville, FL 32611-5530
Phone: 1-352-392-0375
Fax: 1-352-392-7682
World Wide Web URL: http://www.latam.ufl.edu/outreach
Email Address: maryr@ufl.edu

Sables in the Northern Land

The Sarobetsu Moor in northern Hokkaido is featured in this video--it is the habitat of the sable. This video documents these animals in Japan.

Availability: Schools, libraries and homeschoolers in Alabama, Georgia, North Carolina, South Carolina, and Virginia.
Suggested Grade: 6-12
Order Number: 029
Production Date: 1993
Format: VHS videotape
Terms: Borrower pays return postage. Two tapes may be borrowed at a time. Return within 7 days after receipt. Reservations may be made by filling the application found on the web site.

Source: Consulate General of Japan, Atlanta
Japan Information Center
One Alliance Center
3500 Lenox Road, Suite 1600
Atlanta, GA 30326
Phone: 1-404-365-9240
Fax: 1-404-240-4311
World Wide Web URL:
http://www.atlanta.us.emb-japan.go.jp
Email Address: info@cgjapanatlanta.org

Sables in the Northern Land

The Sarobetsu Moor in northern Hokkaido is featured in this video--it is the habitat of the sable. This video documents these animals in Japan.

Availability: Schools, libraries, and nursing homes in Hawaii.
Suggested Grade: 6-12
Order Number: NA-20
Production Date: 1993
Format: VHS videotape
Terms: Borrower pays return postage. A maximum of 3 videos may be borrowed per person. Return within one week of date borrowed.

Source: Consulate General of Japan, Honolulu
1742 Nuuanu Avenue
Honolulu, HI 96817-3294
Phone: 1-808-543-3111
Fax: 1-808-543-3170
World Wide Web URL:
http://www.honolulu.us.emb-japan.go.jp

Salmon Homing Instincts

Follows the interesting lifestyle of the salmon and how they find their way back to the stream in which they were hatched.

Availability: All requesters
Suggested Grade: 3-9
Order Number: not applicable
Format: Online Lesson Plan

Source: Deborah A. Werner
World Wide Web URL:
http://www.eduref.org/Virtual/Lessons/Science/
Animals/ANM0049.html

 Indicates an Internet Resource--just enter the URL and instantly access the FREE teaching aid you need!
All materials listed in this 2010-2011 edition are ***BRAND NEW!***

91

NATURE STUDY

Saving Inky

A documentary about Inky, a pygmy sperm whale who became ill when she ate plastic debris. The malnourishment caused her to beach herself in New Jersey. She was transported to the National Aquarium in Baltimore, rehabilitated, and set free.

Availability:	Schools, libraries, and homeschoolers in Connecticut, Maine, Massachusetts, New Hampshire, Rhode Island, and Vermont.
Suggested Grade:	7-12
Order Number:	VID 159
Production Date:	1984
Format:	VHS videotape
Terms:	Borrower pays return postage. Return within three weeks of receipt. If the tape you request is available, it will be mailed within 5 business days. If not, you will be notified that this video is already out on loan. No more than three titles may be borrowed by one requestor at a time. No reservations for a specific date will be accepted. It is most efficient to order via the web site.

Source: U. S. Environmental Protection Agency, Region 1
Customer Service Center
One Congress Street, Suite 1100
Boston, MA 02214
World Wide Web URL:
http://yosemite.epa.gov/r1/videolen.nsf/

Science and Photography Through the Microscope

A web site devoted to microscopy science education.

Availability:	All requesters
Suggested Grade:	K-5
Order Number:	not applicable
Format:	Web Site

Source: Dennis Kunkel
World Wide Web URL:
http://education.denniskunkel.com/index.php

Sea Lions: Lessons on the Beach

A community of sea lions annually visits an island in the Gulf of California, where the babies are born and must be taught to swim. Compares seals and sea lions. Details physical characteristics, diet, behaviors, and enemies. The only enemy this "grizzly bear of the sea" cannot fight is fishing boats.

Availability:	Schools, libraries, and homeschoolers in the United States who serve the hearing impaired.
Suggested Grade:	2-6
Order Number:	13022
Format:	DVD
Special Notes:	Produced by ACG/United Learning.
Terms:	Sponsor pays all transportation costs. Return one week after receipt. Participation is limited to deaf or hard of hearing Americans, their parents, families, teachers, counselors, or others whose use would benefit a deaf or hard of hearing person. Only one person in the audience needs to be hearing impaired. You must register--which is free. These videos are all open-captioned--no special equipment is required for viewing.

Source: Described and Captioned Media Program
National Association of the Deaf
4211 Church Street Ext.
Roebuck, SC 29376
Phone: 1-800-237-6213
Fax: 1-800-538-5636
World Wide Web URL: http://www.dcmp.org

Sea Turtles' Last Dance

Documents what little is known about the extraordinary Kemp's Ridley sea turtles who have been swimming the world's oceans since the time of the dinosaur. Rare archival footage shows 40,000 turtles nesting on the beaches of Mexico in 1947 in contrast to the few currently remaining.

Availability:	Schools in the United States.
Suggested Grade:	9-Adult
Order Number:	order by title
Production Date:	1988
Format:	VHS videotape
Terms:	Borrower pays return postage. Return 14 days after receipt, via USPS including insurance. All borrowers must have a current lending agreement on file with the Outreach program. This agreement is available via the web site or may be requested via phone or fax.

Source: Center for Latin American Studies
University of Florida
319 Grinter Hall
P. O. Box 115530
Gainesville, FL 32611-5530
Phone: 1-352-392-0375
Fax: 1-352-392-7682
World Wide Web URL: http://www.latam.ufl.edu/outreach
Email Address: maryr@ufl.edu

Sea Vent Viewer

An interactive exploration of the ocean floor in and around a hydrothermal vent.

Availability:	All requesters
Suggested Grade:	All ages
Order Number:	not applicable
Format:	Web Site

Source: National Science Foundation
World Wide Web URL:
http://www.nsf.gov/news/overviews/
earth-environ/interactive.jsp

Sericea Lespedeza in Kansas

Detailed information about this serious pest plant in Kansas.

Availability:	One copy to schools, libraries, and homeschoolers world-wide. May be copied.
Suggested Grade:	2-8
Order Number:	Vol 56
Production Date:	2009
Format:	Article
Special Notes:	May also be downloaded from the web site.

Source: Kansas School Naturalist, The
Department of Biology, Box 4050
Emporia State University
Emporia, KS 66801-5087

Phone: 1-620-341-5614
Fax: 1-620-341-5607
World Wide Web URL:
www.emporia.edu/ksn/http://www.emporia.edu/ksn/
Email Address: ksnaturl@emporia.edu

Simply Sharks!

An interactive, interdisciplinary unit that leads you into the deep blue sea.

Availability:	All requesters
Suggested Grade:	K-1
Order Number:	not applicable
Format:	WebQuest

Source: Shelby Madden, et al
World Wide Web URL:
http://projects.edtech.sandi.net/encanto/simplysharks/

Snake Lesson Plans

Here are several lesson plans about these creatures.

Availability:	All requesters
Suggested Grade:	5
Order Number:	not applicable
Format:	Online Lesson Plans

Source: David Wines
World Wide Web URL:
http://www.uoregon.edu/~titus/herp_old/wines.htm

Songbird Story

When songbirds disappear from their neighborhood, two young people fly along one of the bird migration routes in an animated dream to the tropical rain forest where they see how quickly the rain forests in Central and South America are being cut down to make way for people and development. They learn that they have no time to waste in saving the songbirds.

Availability:	Schools, libraries, homeschoolers, and nursing homes in the United States.
Suggested Grade:	All ages
Order Number:	order by title
Production Date:	1994
Format:	VHS videotape
Terms:	Borrower pays return postage. Return the day after scheduled showing, via UPS or Priority Mail, insured for $100.00. Book 4 weeks in advance and include an alternate date. Order should include name of person responsible for handling the video, and complete mailing address. Please mention this Guide when ordering. Tapes may not be duplicated, edited or exhibited for a fee.

Source: Church World Service
Film & Video Library
28606 Phillips Street, P. O. Box 968
Elkhart, IN 46515
Phone: 1-800-297-1516, ext. 338
Fax: 1-574-262-0966
World Wide Web URL: http://www.churchworldservice.org
Email Address: videos@churchworldservice.org

Struggle to Live, The--Kemp's Ridley Sea Turtle

Documents the struggle for survival of the Kemp's Ridley Sea Turtle.

Availability:	Schools, libraries, homeschoolers, and nursing homes in the United States. Send a padded DVD mailer with two ounces postage included.
Suggested Grade:	5-12
Order Number:	order by title
Format:	DVD
Special Notes:	**May be retained permanently.**

Source: HEART
(Help Endangered Animals-Ridley Turtles)
Attn: Carole H. Allen
P. O. Box 681231
Houston, TX 77268-1231
Phone: 1-281-444-6204
Fax: 1-281-444-6204
World Wide Web URL: http://www.ridleyturtles.org

Taking Apart Owl Pellets

Provides students with a hands on activity to enhance their awareness of an ecosystem by dissecting an owl pellet--a very interesting experiment.

Availability:	All requesters
Suggested Grade:	3-8
Order Number:	not applicable
Format:	Online Lesson Plan

Source: Linda Warner
World Wide Web URL:
http://www.eduref.org/Virtual/Lessons/Science/
Animals/ANM0057.html

Tardigrades: Bears of the Moss

Describes these unique little animals that can stop living for long periods of time. Includes a description of the anatomy and life history of these creatures.

Availability:	One copy to schools, libraries, and homeschoolers world-wide. May be copied.
Suggested Grade:	5-Adult
Order Number:	Vol. 43, No. 3
Production Date:	1996
Format:	Article
Special Notes:	May also be downloaded from the web site.

Source: Kansas School Naturalist, The
Department of Biology, Box 4050
Emporia State University
Emporia, KS 66801-5087
Phone: 1-620-341-5614
Fax: 1-620-341-5607
World Wide Web URL:
www.emporia.edu/ksn/http://www.emporia.edu/ksn/
Email Address: ksnaturl@emporia.edu

Teacher's Guides

Here are a number of teacher's guides (all downloadable) for teaching students about how people interact with the environment and how we can best care for Earth's resources.

 Indicates an Internet Resource--just enter the URL and instantly access the FREE teaching aid you need!
All materials listed in this 2010-2011 edition are BRAND NEW!

93

Availability: All requesters
Suggested Grade: All ages
Order Number: not applicable
Format: Downloadable Teacher's Guides
Source: Sea World/Busch Gardens
World Wide Web URL:
http://www.seaworld.org/just-for-teachers/guides/index.htm

Threatened and Endangered Species of West Virginia

Lists and describes endangered and threatened plant and animal species in West Virginia.

Availability: Classroom quantities to schools, libraries, and homeschoolers in the United States.
Suggested Grade: 3-12
Order Number: order by title
Format: Brochure
Source: West Virginia Wildlife Resources Section
West Virginia Division of Natural Resources
324 Fourth Avenue
South Charleston, WV 25303
Phone: 1-304-558-2771
Fax: 1-304-558-3147
World Wide Web URL: http://www.wvdnr.gov

Triumph of the Wood Duck

An overview of the behavior patterns, physical characteristics and feeding habits of this perching duck.

Availability: Schools, libraries, homeschoolers, and nursing homes in Illinois, Indiana, Iowa, Michigan, Minnesota, Missouri, Ohio, and Wisconsin only.
Suggested Grade: K-12
Order Number: 372A
Format: VHS videotape
Terms: Return postage is paid by borrower. Book 10-14 days in advance. Return 7 days after showing. Please provide alternate showing date.
Source: U. S. Fish and Wildlife Service
Region 3, Resource Library
3815 American Boulevard
Bloomington, MN 55425
Fax: 1-612-725-3279
Email Address: judy_geck@fws.gov

Visiting a Meadow Habitat: An Introduction to Field Study

Teaches students through inquiry about the importance of pollinators and their relationship within a meadow ecosystem.

Availability: All requesters
Suggested Grade: 3-5
Order Number: not applicable
Format: Online Lesson Plan
Source: Wildlife Habitat Council
World Wide Web URL:
http://www.wildlifehc.org/managementtools/
backyard-lessonplans.cfm

Welcome to the Incredible World of Mammals

All sorts of information about mammals.

Availability: All requesters
Suggested Grade: 4-12
Order Number: not applicable
Format: Web Site
Source: Earth-Life Web Productions
World Wide Web URL:
http://www.earthlife.net/mammals/welcome.html

Wetlands and Fisheries

Explores how wetlands support diverse fish communities, types of wetlands used by fish, and contacts for more information.

Availability: Single copies to schools, libraries, and homeschoolers world-wide. May be copied for classroom distribution.
Suggested Grade: 6-12
Order Number: FS-063
Format: Fact Sheet
Special Notes: May also be downloaded from the web site.
Source: Ohio Sea Grant Publications
Attn: Nancy Cruickshank
1314 Kinnear Road
Columbus, OH 43212-1194
Phone: 1-614-292-8949
Fax: 1-614-292-4364
World Wide Web URL:
http://www.ohioseagrant.osu.edu/publications/

WhaleNet

Not only provides information about whales, but allows students and teachers to share information as well.

Availability: All requesters
Suggested Grade: K-12
Order Number: not applicable
Format: Web Site
Source: Wheelock College
World Wide Web URL:
http://whale.wheelock.edu/Welcome.html

Whale Songs

A resource for teachers, students, and whale lovers.

Availability: All requesters
Suggested Grade: All ages
Order Number: not applicable
Format: Web Site
Source: Lance Leonhardt
World Wide Web URL: http://www.whalesongs.org

Whale Watch

Students will learn about 65 living species of toothed whales and about 11 living species of baleen whales.

Availability: All requesters
Suggested Grade: 4-6
Order Number: not applicable
Format: WebQuest

Source: Kathi Ligocki
World Wide Web URL:
http://members.fortunecity.com/kligocki/

Where Do Animals Go In Winter?

Animals living in cold climates adapt to winter temperatures and the scarcity of food in different ways. Birds migrate to warmer climates; other animals change their behavior, diet, shelter, and even their appearance. See what animals do to prepare for winter, how they survive during the cold months, and their response to warming spring days.

Availability: Schools, libraries, and homeschoolers in the United States who serve the hearing impaired.
Suggested Grade: 1-6
Order Number: 12354
Production Date: 1995
Format: DVD
Special Notes: Produced by National Geographic Society.
Terms: Sponsor pays all transportation costs. Return one week after receipt. Participation is limited to deaf or hard of hearing Americans, their parents, families, teachers, counselors, or others whose use would benefit a deaf or hard of hearing person. Only one person in the audience needs to be hearing impaired. You must register--which is free. These videos are all open-captioned--no special equipment is required for viewing.

Source: Described and Captioned Media Program
National Association of the Deaf
4211 Church Street Ext.
Roebuck, SC 29376
Phone: 1-800-237-6213
Fax: 1-800-538-5636
World Wide Web URL: http://www.dcmp.org

Who Dunnit?

Learn how to be a crime solver by studying how forensic scientists analyze evidence.

Availability: All requesters
Suggested Grade: 6-8
Order Number: not applicable
Format: Web Site

Source: Linda C. Joseph and Linda D. Resch
World Wide Web URL:
http://www.cyberbee.com/whodunnit/crime.html

Wild Birds of Taiwan

Located in the northwest Pacific, in tropical and subtropical zones, Taiwan is a common stopping-off point for migrating birds, and home to 400 species of birds, 14 endemic species found nowhere else. Chinese bulbuls like people and follow them from the lowlands to the highlands. Features splendid photography.

Availability: Schools, libraries, and nursing homes in the United States and Canada.
Suggested Grade: All ages
Order Number: TV013
Format: VHS videotape

Terms: Borrower pays return postage. Return with 14 days after scheduled showing, via UPS or U. S. Mail. All requests must included an educational institution affiliation, a current address, and phone number. Order through web site only.

Source: Cornell University East Asia Program
World Wide Web URL:
http://www.einaudi.cornell.edu/eastasia/outreach/video.asp
Email Address: east_asia1@cornell.edu

Wildcats

The program explores the wild cats--Jaguar, Mountain Lion, Lynx, Bobcat, Margay, Ocelot, and Jagurindi. In form and function, wildcats reach the peak of predatory evolution.

Availability: Schools, libraries, homeschoolers, and nursing homes in Illinois, Indiana, Iowa, Michigan, Minnesota, Missouri, Ohio, and Wisconsin only.
Suggested Grade: 4-12
Order Number: 163
Format: VHS videotape
Terms: Return postage is paid by borrower. Book 10-14 days in advance. Return 7 days after showing. Please provide alternate showing date.

Source: U. S. Fish and Wildlife Service
Region 3, Resource Library
3815 American Boulevard
Bloomington, MN 55425
Fax: 1-612-725-3279
Email Address: judy_geck@fws.gov

WildFinder

A map-driven, searchable database of more than 26,000 species worldwide, with a powerful search tool that allows users to discover where species live or explore wild places to find out what species live there.

Availability: All requesters
Suggested Grade: 6-12
Order Number: not applicable
Format: Web Site

Source: World Wildlife Fund
World Wide Web URL:
http://www.worldwildlife.org/wildfinder/

Winged Wisdom

A pet bird e-zine for exotic birds and pet parrots.

Availability: All requesters
Suggested Grade: All ages
Order Number: not applicable
Format: Online Magazine
Special Notes: No new editions have been published recently but informative articles are still on-line.

Source: Birds n Ways
World Wide Web URL:
http://www.birdsnways.com/wisdom/

Indicates an Internet Resource--just enter the URL and instantly access the FREE teaching aid you need!
All materials listed in this 2010-2011 edition are BRAND NEW!

95

Wolf Spiders: Lab Exercises Investigating Distribution, Abundance and Behavior of Wolf Spiders

A virtual seminar for learning about these spiders.

Availability:	All requesters
Suggested Grade:	6-12
Order Number:	not applicable
Format:	Web Site

Source: Gail E. Stratton
World Wide Web URL:
http://www.accessexcellence.org/LC/SS/
wolf_spider/intro.html

World of Insects (Series)

Live-action, close-up, color photography brings viewers into an incredible unseen insect world.

Availability:	Schools, libraries, homeschoolers, and nursing homes in Illinois, Indiana, Iowa, Michigan, Minnesota, Missouri, Ohio, and Wisconsin only.
Suggested Grade:	K-12
Order Number:	167-169
Format:	VHS videotape
Terms:	Return postage is paid by borrower. Book 10-14 days in advance. Return 7 days after showing. Please provide alternate showing date.

Source: U. S. Fish and Wildlife Service
Region 3, Resource Library
3815 American Boulevard
Bloomington, MN 55425
Fax: 1-612-725-3279
Email Address: judy_geck@fws.gov

Year In White-Tail Country

Stunning photography and an absorbing soundtrack will immerse you in the secluded environment of the Whitetail Deer. Examine the Whitetail's life cycle and social structure.

Availability:	Schools, libraries, homeschoolers, and nursing homes in Illinois, Indiana, Iowa, Michigan, Minnesota, Missouri, Ohio, and Wisconsin only.
Suggested Grade:	5-12
Order Number:	170
Format:	VHS videotape
Terms:	Return postage is paid by borrower. Book 10-14 days in advance. Return 7 days after showing. Please provide alternate showing date.

Source: U. S. Fish and Wildlife Service
Region 3, Resource Library
3815 American Boulevard
Bloomington, MN 55425
Fax: 1-612-725-3279
Email Address: judy_geck@fws.gov

Year of the Eagle

Following the life of the Bald Eagle, from birth through first flight to maturity, this program shows that saving the eagle has become symbolic of the need to balance technological advances with preservation of the natural environment. Contains an eagle autopsy scene.

Availability:	Schools, libraries, homeschoolers, and nursing homes in Illinois, Indiana, Iowa, Michigan, Minnesota, Missouri, Ohio, and Wisconsin only.
Suggested Grade:	3-12
Order Number:	171
Format:	VHS videotape
Terms:	Return postage is paid by borrower. Book 10-14 days in advance. Return 7 days after showing. Please provide alternate showing date.

Source: U. S. Fish and Wildlife Service
Region 3, Resource Library
3815 American Boulevard
Bloomington, MN 55425
Fax: 1-612-725-3279
World Wide Web URL:
Email Address: judy_geck@fws.gov

Yukon Butterflies

A colorful booklet all about butterflies.

Availability:	All requesters
Suggested Grade:	4-Adult
Order Number:	not applicable
Format:	Downloadable booklet
Special Notes:	This is a PDF file which will open automatically on your computer.

Source: Government of Yukon
World Wide Web URL:
http://www.environmentyukon.gov.yk.ca/pdf/
YukonButterflieswebfinal05.pdf

Ask the Experts

You can pose a question or find out the answers to questions previously asked by others.

Availability: All requesters
Suggested Grade: 9-Adult
Order Number: not applicable
Format: Web Site

Source: PhysLink.com
World Wide Web URL:
http://www.physlink.com/Education/AskExperts/Index.cfm

Atlas

For architects and construction engineers--computes the resulting moments and reaction forces for a given beam with loads applied to is, using Cross' method.

Availability: All requesters
Suggested Grade: 9-Adult
Order Number: not applicable
Format: Downloadable FULL PROGRAM

Source: Rekenwonder Software
World Wide Web URL:
http://www.rekenwonder.com/index.html

Big Melt, The

This science lesson will introduce students to the three phases of matter by analyzing ice melting.

Availability: All requesters
Suggested Grade: 4-12
Order Number: not applicable
Format: Online Lesson Plan

Source: Shirley Willingham
World Wide Web URL: http://teachertech.rice.edu/
Participants/swilling/
lessons2/bigmelt/studentpages/index.html

Birth of Oroville Dam, The

Oroville Dam is the tallest dam in the United States. This video shows historic highlights of the dam's construction from ground breaking through its dedication by Ronald Reagan.

Availability: Schools, libraries, homeschoolers, and nursing homes in the United States.
Suggested Grade: 6-Adult
Order Number: order by title
Format: DVD
Special Notes: A number of titles from this organization are included on this DVD.
Terms: Borrower pays return postage. Return within 14 days after scheduled use, via UPS or Federal Express. Book at least 14 days in advance and include alternate date. Requests should include title(s), format, name of responsible person, organizational affiliation, phone, and complete delivery address. No part of any program can be used or duplicated without prior written permission. All programs are available for purchase at a nominal fee. May be available in other formats; inquire if interested. Online video previews are available.

Source: California Department of Water Resources
Attn: Video Library, Room 204-22
P. O. Box 942836
Sacramento, CA 94236-0001
Phone: 1-916-653-4893
Fax: 1-916-653-3310
World Wide Web URL: http://www.water.ca.gov/
Email Address: www.publicawillm@water.ca.gov

Birth of Oroville Dam, The

Oroville Dam is the tallest dam in the United States. This video shows historic highlights of the dam's construction from ground breaking through its dedication by Ronald Reagan.

Availability: Schools, libraries, homeschoolers, and nursing homes in the United States.
Suggested Grade: 6-Adult
Order Number: order by title
Format: VHS videotape
Special Notes: Closed captioned.
Terms: Borrower pays return postage. Return within 14 days after scheduled use, via UPS or Federal Express. Book at least 14 days in advance and include alternate date. Requests should include title(s), format, name of responsible person, organizational affiliation, phone, and complete delivery address. No part of any program can be used or duplicated without prior written permission. All programs are available for purchase at a nominal fee. May be available in other formats; inquire if interested. Online video previews are available.

Source: California Department of Water Resources
Attn: Video Library, Room 204-22
P. O. Box 942836
Sacramento, CA 94236-0001
Phone: 1-916-653-4893
Fax: 1-916-653-3310
World Wide Web URL: http://www.water.ca.gov/
Email Address: www.publicawillm@water.ca.gov

Center for History of Physics, The

Provides exhibits, sample syllabi, and many other resources for physics history and its allied fields.

Availability: All requesters
Suggested Grade: 6-12
Order Number: not applicable
Format: Web Site

Source: American Institute of Physics
World Wide Web URL: http://aip.org/history/index.html

Classroom Energy!

Provides activities and resources for learning all about energy.

Availability: All requesters
Suggested Grade: 6-8
Order Number: not applicable
Format: Web Site

Source: American Petroleum Institute
World Wide Web URL: http://www.classroom-energy.org/

Indicates an Internet Resource--just enter the URL and instantly access the FREE teaching aid you need!
All materials listed in this 2010-2011 edition are BRAND NEW!

97

Digital Simulator

Electronic design automation software (without the $50,000 price tag.)

Availability:	Educational institutions and students.
Suggested Grade:	9-Adult
Platform:	Windows
Order Number:	not applicable
Format:	Downloadable FULL PROGRAM

Source: Ara Knaian
World Wide Web URL:
http://web.mit.edu/ara/www/ds.html

Don't Burn, Build!

You are part of an elite engineering team, personally invited by the Indian government, to participate in a major competition to design a new bridge for the city of Calcutta, or Kolkata.

Availability:	All requesters
Suggested Grade:	9-12
Order Number:	not applicable
Format:	WebQuest

Source: Kate Kairys, Katie O'Gorman, and Alice Chen
World Wide Web URL:
http://oncampus.richmond.edu/academics/education/
projects/webquests/bridge/

Electricity from Nuclear Energy

Explains and illustrates how nuclear power generates electricity.

Availability:	One copy to schools, libraries, and homeschoolers in the United States and Canada.
Suggested Grade:	4-10
Order Number:	order by title
Format:	Booklet

Source: Westinghouse Electric Company
Communications Department
4350 Northern Pike
Pittsburgh, PA 15146-2886
Fax: 1-412-374-3272
World Wide Web URL:
http://www.westinghousenuclear.com

Eloquent Logic: A World of Physics and Math

A game web site that teaches the fundamental principles of physics.

Availability:	All requesters
Suggested Grade:	9-12
Order Number:	not applicable
Format:	Web Site
Special Notes:	This URL will lead you to a subject page. Then click on the appropriate subject heading.

Source: ThinkQuest
World Wide Web URL:
http://www.thinkquest.org/pls/html/think.library

Energy

Kate uses moving toys to show Jeffrey the basic principles of energy, the different forms it can take, and how energy is found everywhere. They make two simple toys to experiment with energy.

Availability:	Schools, libraries, and homeschoolers in the United States who serve the hearing impaired.
Suggested Grade:	2-6
Order Number:	12834
Production Date:	1994
Format:	DVD
Special Notes:	Produced by Films for the Humanities & Sciences.
Terms:	Sponsor pays all transportation costs. Return one week after receipt. Participation is limited to deaf or hard of hearing Americans, their parents, families, teachers, counselors, or others whose use would benefit a deaf or hard of hearing person. Only one person in the audience needs to be hearing impaired. You must register--which is free. These videos are all open-captioned--no special equipment is required for viewing.

Source: Described and Captioned Media Program
National Association of the Deaf
4211 Church Street Ext.
Roebuck, SC 29376
Phone: 1-800-237-6213
Fax: 1-800-538-5636
World Wide Web URL: http://www.dcmp.org

Fear of Physics

Demonstrates physics in action.

Availability:	All requesters
Suggested Grade:	All ages
Order Number:	not applicable
Format:	Web Site

Source: FearOfPhysics.com
World Wide Web URL: http://www.fearofphysics.com/

Friction, Forces and Motion

Here are some activities and websites to use when teaching and learning about friction, forces, and motion.

Availability:	All requesters
Suggested Grade:	4-8
Order Number:	not applicable
Format:	Online Lesson Plans

Source: Robin Ann Henry
World Wide Web URL:
http://teachertech.rice.edu/Participants/
rhenry/Lessons/frfomo/index.html

Galloping Gertie

In this unit students explore bridges and the various forces that affect their stability.

Availability:	All requesters
Suggested Grade:	5-12
Order Number:	not applicable
Format:	Online Lesson Plan

Source: Shirley Willingham
World Wide Web URL:
http://teachertech.rice.edu/Participants/swilling/
lessons2/bridges/kidpages/index.html

Geo U

An integrated union for high school math and science allows students to create their own university, from buildings to landscape

Availability: All requesters
Suggested Grade: 9-12
Order Number: not applicable
Format: WebQuest

Source: Tony Robbins & Steve Bjork
World Wide Web URL:
http://www.yorkville.k12.il.us/webquests/
webqrobbjork/webqsrobbjork.html

It's So Simple

An introduction to simple machines.

Availability: All requesters
Suggested Grade: 6-12
Order Number: not applicable
Format: Online Lesson Plan

Source: Kimberly Baker-Brownfield and Jacques Marquette Branch
World Wide Web URL:
http://www.iit.edu/~smile/mp0298.htm

Kids Design Network

Students will investigate a challenge, dream up a design, and draw up plans. Includes a teacher's guide.

Availability: All requesters
Suggested Grade: 3-8
Order Number: not applicable
Format: Web Site

Source: DuPage Children's Museum
World Wide Web URL:
http://www.dupagechildrensmuseum.org/kdn/

Magnets

Teaches students all about magnets and how they attract.

Availability: All requesters
Suggested Grade: 4-12
Order Number: not applicable
Format: Online Lesson Plan

Source: Consuela Llamas
World Wide Web URL:
http://teachertech.rice.edu/Participants/cllamas/lessons/
science/magnets/studentmagnets.htm

MagVar

Computes and displays magnetic variation for anywhere in the world.

Availability: All requesters
Suggested Grade: 9-Adult
Platform: Windows
Order Number: not applicable

Format: Downloadable FULL PROGRAM
Source: Pangolin Communications
World Wide Web URL:
http://www.pangolin.co.nz/free_stuff.php

Modeling Instruction in High School Physics

Provides information about the modeling method for high school physics.

Availability: All requesters
Suggested Grade: 9-12
Order Number: not applicable
Format: Web Site

Source: Arizona State University
World Wide Web URL:
http://modeling.asu.edu/modeling-HS.html

Motion Mountain: The Physics Textbook

Over 1200 pages; here is a complete physics textbook.

Availability: All requesters
Suggested Grade: 6-12
Order Number: not applicable
Format: Downloadable Book

Source: Christoph Schiller
World Wide Web URL: http://www.motionmountain.net/

Particle Adventure

Introduces the standard model theory of fundamental particles and forces.

Availability: All requesters
Suggested Grade: 9-12
Languages: English; French; Polish; Spanish
Order Number: not applicable
Format: Web Site

Source: Particle Data Group
World Wide Web URL: http://particleadventure.org

Peggy E. Schweiger's Physics Site

Includes lesson plans, lab forms, and quizzes for physics teachers and students alike.

Availability: All requesters
Suggested Grade: 9-12
Order Number: not applicable
Format: Web Site

Source: Peggy Schweiger
World Wide Web URL:
http://teachertech.rice.edu/Participants/pschweig/
lessonlink.html

Physics in a Bag

A nine week lesson that will teach students what physics is all about.

Availability: All requesters
Suggested Grade: 4-8
Order Number: not applicable
Format: Online Lesson Plan

Source: Shirley Willingham
World Wide Web URL: http://teachertech.rice.edu/
Participants/swilling/lessons2/physicsbag4/studentmenu.htm

 Indicates an Internet Resource--just enter the URL and instantly access the FREE teaching aid you need!
All materials listed in this 2010-2011 edition are BRAND NEW!

99

Physics Education Journal

Here is the online version of the Physics Education Journal. Many of the articles available through the printed magazine are available online.

Availability:	All requesters
Suggested Grade:	9-12
Order Number:	not applicable
Format:	Online Magazine

Source: Institute of Physics
World Wide Web URL: http://www.iop.org/Journals/pe

Physics Education Technology

Simulations of physical phenomena for teaching and learning physics.

Availability:	All requesters
Suggested Grade:	9-12
Languages:	English; Spanish
Order Number:	not applicable
Format:	Web Site

Source: PhET Project, The
World Wide Web URL:
http://phet.colorado.edu/web-pages/simulations-base.html

PhysicsFront.org

Lesson plans, activities, teacher resources, and much more. For high school students learning physics, but the sight contains a great section of physical science in grades K-8.

Availability:	All requesters
Suggested Grade:	K-12
Order Number:	not applicable
Format:	Web Site
Special Notes:	You must register, but registration is free.

Source: American Association of Physics Teachers
World Wide Web URL:
http://www.compadre.org/precollege/index.cfm

Physics Question of the Week, The

Each week a new question is posted and the answer for the previous question of the week is posted. The questions involve real experimental physics.

Availability:	All requesters
Suggested Grade:	9-12
Order Number:	not applicable
Format:	Web Site

Source: University of Maryland Department of Physics
World Wide Web URL:
http://www.physics.umd.edu/lecdem/outreach/
QOTW/active/questions.htm

Physics with Yoder

Explores all areas of physics.

Availability:	All requesters
Suggested Grade:	9-Adult
Order Number:	not applicable
Format:	Online Lesson Plans

Source: Gloria Yoder
World Wide Web URL:
http://teachertech.rice.edu/Participants/gyoder/

Physics Zone, The

A web site devoted to being a resource for learning introductory level, algebra based, physics. Includes lessons, tutorials, and reviews.

Availability:	All requesters
Suggested Grade:	9-12
Order Number:	not applicable
Format:	Web Site

Source: Science Joy Wagon
World Wide Web URL:
http://www.sciencejoywagon.com/physicszone

Powering the World: The Energy That Fuels Us

Explains fossil fuel, hydroelectric, wind, solar, and nuclear energy.

Availability:	All requesters
Suggested Grade:	4-12
Order Number:	not applicable
Format:	Web Site
Special Notes:	This URL will lead you to a subject page. Then click on the appropriate subject heading.

Source: ThinkQuest
World Wide Web URL:
http://www.thinkquest.org/pls/html/think.library

Practical Physics Lessons

Here are a number of physics lesson plans written to make the study of physics fun.

Availability:	All requesters
Suggested Grade:	9-Adult
Order Number:	not applicable
Format:	Online Lesson Plans

Source: C. Johnson
World Wide Web URL:
http://mb-soft.com/public/phys0.html

Project A t o m i c

From simple topics like "what is radiation?" to more difficult ones like "Half-life," each quiz builds on each lesson.

Availability:	All requesters
Suggested Grade:	4-12
Order Number:	not applicable
Format:	Web Site
Special Notes:	This URL will lead you to a subject page. Then click on the appropriate subject heading.

Source: ThinkQuest
World Wide Web URL:
http://www.thinkquest.org/pls/html/think.library

RoboMates

A robot is a very helpful invention that serves humanity in a wide range of applications.

Availability:	All requesters
Suggested Grade:	4-12
Order Number:	not applicable
Format:	Web Site

Special Notes: This URL will lead you to a subject page.
                   Then click on the appropriate subject heading.
Source: ThinkQuest
World Wide Web URL:
http://www.thinkquest.org/pls/html/think.library

ROVer Ranch
Presents resources for teaching and learning about robotic engineering and more about robotic systems.
Availability: All requesters
Suggested Grade: K-12
Order Number: not applicable
Format: Web Site
Source: NASA Johnson Space Center
World Wide Web URL: http://prime.jsc.nasa.gov/ROV/

Simple Machines
Real-life examples demonstrate the function and purpose of the six simple machines: the inclined plane, the wedge, the screw, the lever, the wheel and axle, and the pulley.
Availability: Schools, libraries, and homeschoolers in the
                   United States who serve the hearing impaired.
Suggested Grade: 4-8
Order Number: 12926
Production Date: 1999
Format: DVD
Terms: Sponsor pays all transportation costs. Return one week after receipt. Participation is limited to deaf or hard of hearing Americans, their parents, families, teachers, counselors, or others whose use would benefit a deaf or hard of hearing person. Only one person in the audience needs to be hearing impaired. You must register--which is free. These videos are all open-captioned--no special equipment is required for viewing.
Source: Described and Captioned Media Program
National Association of the Deaf
4211 Church Street Ext.
Roebuck, SC 29376
Phone: 1-800-237-6213
Fax: 1-800-538-5636
World Wide Web URL: http://www.dcmp.org

Watt's That?!
"The only Internet Energy Game Show." Available in several versions.
Availability: All requesters
Suggested Grade: All ages
Order Number: not applicable
Format: Web Site
Source: California Energy Commission
World Wide Web URL:
http://www.energyquest.ca.gov/games/index.html

What Objects Sink and What Objects Float
Students will explore why certain objects sink and why certain objects float. Especially written for severe and profound non-categorical special education students.
Availability: All requesters
Suggested Grade: 1-8
Order Number: not applicable
Format: Online Lesson Plan
Source: Michael Young
World Wide Web URL:
http://www.iit.edu/~smile/chbi2200.htm

Wonderful Wacky World of Atoms
Study of atoms for young students.
Availability: All requesters
Suggested Grade: 3-8
Order Number: not applicable
Format: Web Site
Special Notes: This URL will lead you to a subject page.
                   Then click on the appropriate subject heading.
Source: ThinkQuest
World Wide Web URL:
http://www.thinkquest.org/pls/html/think.library

 Indicates an Internet Resource--just enter the URL and instantly access the FREE teaching aid you need!
All materials listed in this 2010-2011 edition are BRAND NEW!

101

Accountability Mechanisms in Big City School Systems

Discusses how big city school systems can achieve accountability.

Availability: All requesters
Suggested Grade: Teacher Reference
Order Number: not applicable
Production Date: 1991
Format: Online Article
Source: Linda Darling-Hammond
World Wide Web URL: http://www.ericdigests.org/
pre-9220/big.htm

Action Research in Science Education

Provides an introduction to action research in science education.

Availability: All requesters
Suggested Grade: Teacher Reference
Order Number: not applicable
Production Date: 2000
Format: Online Article
Source: Allan Feldman and Brenda Capobianco
World Wide Web URL: http://www.ericdigests.org/
2003-1/action.htm

Aggression and Cooperation: Helping Young Children Develop Constructive Strategies

Explores this issue in a concise report.

Availability: All requesters
Suggested Grade: Teacher Reference
Order Number: not applicable
Production Date: 1992
Format: Online Article
Source: Jan Jewett
World Wide Web URL: http://www.ericdigests.org/
1992-1/young.htm

Benefits of Mixed-Age Grouping, The

Explores this issue in a concise report.

Availability: All requesters
Suggested Grade: Teacher Reference
Order Number: not applicable
Production Date: 1995
Format: Online Article
Source: Lilian G. Katz
World Wide Web URL:
http://www.ericdigests.org/1996-1/mixed.htm

Block Scheduling: Structuring Time to Achieve National Standards in Mathematics and Science

Discusses this topic.

Availability: All requesters
Suggested Grade: Teacher Reference
Order Number: not applicable
Format: Online Article
Source: Bernard Durkin
World Wide Web URL: http://www.ericdigests.org/
2000-1/block.html

Charter Challenge, The

Discusses how charter schools can succeed in teaching certain students.

Availability: All requesters
Suggested Grade: Teacher Reference
Order Number: not applicable
Format: Online Article
Source: Brian Hanson-Harding
World Wide Web URL:
http://teacher.scholastic.com/professional/
teachertoteacher/charter_challenge.htm

Classroom Organization

Use social studies skills for everyday tasks, establishing a seating chart and reviewing map reading.

Availability: All requesters
Suggested Grade: 6-12
Order Number: not applicable
Format: Online Lesson Plan
Source: Thomas M. Hays
World Wide Web URL:
http://www.col-ed.org/cur/sst/sst50.txt

Conflict Resolution Programs in Schools

Discusses how to set up these programs.

Availability: All requesters
Suggested Grade: Teacher Reference
Order Number: not applicable
Production Date: 1991
Format: Online Article
Source: Morton Inger
World Wide Web URL:
http://www.ericdigests.org/1992-5/conflict.htm

Deteriorating School Facilities and Student Learning

Explores the impact of deteriorating school conditions on student learning and discusses what can be done until more funds become available to improve conditions.

Availability: All requesters
Suggested Grade: Teacher Reference
Order Number: not applicable
Production Date: 1993
Format: Online Article
Source: Linda M. Frazier
World Wide Web URL:
http://www.ericdigests.org/1993/school.htm

Determining the Existence of Gender Bias in Daily Tasks

Demonstrates how role responsibilities in the every day environment of home remain based in stereotyping to a great degree.

Availability: All requesters
Suggested Grade: 3-6
Order Number: not applicable
Format: Online Lesson Plan

Source: Kathleen E. van Noort
World Wide Web URL:
http://www.ricw.state.ri.us/lessons/135.htm

Developing Instructional Leaders

Reviews the demands of today's instructional leadership and discusses steps that universities and school districts can take to help leaders develop the necessary skills.

Availability:	All requesters
Suggested Grade:	Teacher Reference
Order Number:	not applicable
Production Date:	2002
Format:	Online Article

Source: Larry Lashway
World Wide Web URL:
http://www.ericdigests.org/2003-2/leaders.html

Dispositions as Educational Goals

Explores this issue in a concise report.

Availability:	All requesters
Suggested Grade:	Teacher Reference
Order Number:	not applicable
Production Date:	1993
Format:	Online Article

Source: Lilian G. Katz
World Wide Web URL:
http://www.ericdigests.org/1994/goals.htm

Dr. Mac's Amazing Behavior Management Advice Site

Offers thousands of tips on managing student behavior, and provides step-by-step directions for implementing a great number of standard interventions. Also contains a bulletin board.

Availability:	All requesters
Suggested Grade:	Adult
Order Number:	not applicable
Format:	Web Site

Source: Thomas McIntyre
World Wide Web URL: http://www.behavioradvisor.com/

Empowering Culturally and Linguistically Diverse Students with Learning Problems

Provides a basic overview, plus pertinent references, on this topic.

Availability:	All requesters
Suggested Grade:	Teacher Reference
Languages:	English: Spanish
Order Number:	not applicable
Production Date:	1991
Format:	Online Article

Source: Jim Cummins
World Wide Web URL:
http://www.ericdigests.org/pre-9220/problems.htm

Engaging the Community to Support Student Achievement

Examines how public engagement can foster student achievement, how school boards and administrations can facilitate the public-engagement process, and how school leaders can solicit enduring support from key stakeholders.

Availability:	All requesters
Suggested Grade:	Teacher Reference
Order Number:	not applicable
Production Date:	2002
Format:	Online Article

Source: Chris Cunningham
World Wide Web URL:
http://www.ericdigests.org/2003-1/student.htm

Enhancing the Communication Skills of Newly-Arrived Asian American Students

Provides information on helping these new students adjust.

Availability:	All requesters
Suggested Grade:	Teacher Reference
Order Number:	not applicable
Production Date:	1998
Format:	Online Article

Source: Li Rong Lilly Cheng
World Wide Web URL:
http://www.ericdigests.org/1999-1/asian.html

Expectations for Students

Discusses having realistic expectations for students.

Availability:	All requesters
Suggested Grade:	Teacher Reference
Order Number:	not applicable
Production Date:	1997
Format:	Online Article

Source: Linda Lumsden
World Wide Web URL:
http://www.ericdigests.org/1998-1/expectations.htm

Five Tricky Personalities and How to Handle Them

Use positive behavior management to keep even "difficult" students focused on learning.

Availability:	All requesters
Suggested Grade:	Teacher Reference
Order Number:	not applicable
Format:	Online Article

Source: Bill Rogers
World Wide Web URL:
http://teacher.scholastic.com/professional/classmgmt/
trickypersons.htm

Focus on After-School Time for Violence Prevention

Examines the results of after-school programs in reducing crime.

Availability:	All requesters
Suggested Grade:	Teacher Reference
Languages:	English; Spanish
Order Number:	not applicable
Production Date:	2001
Format:	Online Article

Source: Peggy Patten and Anne S. Robertson
World Wide Web URL:
http://www.ericdigests.org/2002-2/focus.htm

 Indicates an Internet Resource--just enter the URL and instantly access the FREE teaching aid you need!
*All materials listed in this 2010-2011 edition are **BRAND NEW!***

103

Fundamentals of School Security, The
Discusses this "front-burner" issue for educators, students, and citizens.

Availability: All requesters
Suggested Grade: Teacher Reference
Order Number: not applicable
Production Date: 1999
Format: Online Article
Source: Joan Gaustad
World Wide Web URL:
http://www.ericdigests.org/2000-3/security.htm

Grouping Students for Instruction in Middle Schools
Discusses attitudes toward tracking in middle school and summarizes recent research on ability grouping and tracking.

Availability: All requesters
Suggested Grade: Teacher Reference
Order Number: not applicable
Production Date: 1998
Format: Online Article
Source: Rebecca Mills
World Wide Web URL:
http://www.ericdigests.org/1999-1/grouping.html

Helping Middle School Students Make the Transition to High School
Information to help students make this sometimes difficult transition.

Availability: All requesters
Suggested Grade: Teacher Reference
Languages: English; Korean
Order Number: not applicable
Production Date: 1999
Format: Online Article
Source: Nancy B. Mizelle
World Wide Web URL:
http://www.ericdigests.org/2000-1/high.html

Higher Standard of Living in Right-to-Work States
Presents a comparison between jobs in right to work states and jobs in forced unionism states.

Availability: Limit of 50 copies to schools, libraries, and homeschoolers in the United States and Canada.
Suggested Grade: Teacher Reference
Order Number: order by title
Production Date: 1999
Format: Brochure
Source: Concerned Educators Against Forced Unionism
Cathy Jones, Director
8001 Braddock Road
Springfield, VA 22160
Phone: 1-703-321-8519
Fax: 1-703-321-7143
World Wide Web URL: http://www.ceafu.org
Email Address: clj@nrtw.org

High School Report Cards
Summarizes trends in grading practices and introduces issues related to standards-based reporting.

Availability: All requesters
Suggested Grade: Teacher Reference
Order Number: not applicable
Production Date: 2003
Format: Online Article
Source: Carol Boston
World Wide Web URL:
http://www.ericdigests.org/2005-2/cards.html

Homeless Children: Addressing the Challenge in Rural Schools
Considers the challenge of homelessness in rural areas, the meaning of homelessness for rural children, and more.

Availability: All requesters
Suggested Grade: Teacher Reference
Order Number: not applicable
Production Date: 1999
Format: Online Article
Source: Yvonne M. Vissing
World Wide Web URL:
http://www.ericdigests.org/1999-3/homeless.htm

How Schools Allocate and Use Their Resources
Summarizes data on expenditures and staffing patterns in the nation's schools, weighs the impact of financial resources on students' educational outcomes, and discusses the implications of these allocation patterns for future policy at both the state and local levels.

Availability: All requesters
Suggested Grade: Teacher Reference
Order Number: not applicable
Production Date: 2000
Format: Online Article
Source: Lawrence O. Picus
World Wide Web URL:
http://findarticles.com/p/articles/mi_pric/
is_200012/ai_2402568331

How Well Are Charter Schools Serving Urban and Minority Students?
Discusses this issue.

Availability: All requesters
Suggested Grade: Teacher Reference
Order Number: not applicable
Production Date: 1996
Format: Online Article
Special Notes: This is a PDF file which will open automatically on your computer.
Source: Wendy Schwartz
World Wide Web URL:
http://www.eric.ed.gov/ERICDocs/data/ericdocs2sql/
content_storage_01/0000019b/80/16/8e/17.pdf

I Love That Teaching Idea
Although a site that sells things, this site also presents a

number of free teaching ideas and reproducibles for elementary classrooms.

Availability:	All requesters
Suggested Grade:	Teacher Reference
Order Number:	not applicable
Format:	Web Site

Source: I Love That Teaching Idea
World Wide Web URL:
http://www.ILoveThatTeachingIdea.com/

Improving Urban Education with Magnet Schools

Explores this topic.

Availability:	All requesters
Suggested Grade:	Teacher Reference
Order Number:	not applicable
Production Date:	1991
Format:	Online Article

Source: Morton Inger
World Wide Web URL:
http://www.ericdigests.org/1992-4/magnet.htm

Inclusion in Middle Schools

Examines this issue.

Availability:	All requesters
Suggested Grade:	Teacher Reference
Languages:	English; Spanish
Order Number:	not applicable
Production Date:	2001
Format:	Online Article

Source: Rebecca A. Hines
World Wide Web URL:
http://www.ericdigests.org/2002-3/inclusion.htm

Instructional Strategies for Migrant Students

Offers research-based guidance for teachers to help them use effective instructional strategies that will build on the strengths that migrant children bring into the classroom.

Availability:	All requesters
Suggested Grade:	Teacher Reference
Order Number:	not applicable
Format:	Online Article

Source: Velma D. Menchaca and Jose A. Ruiz-Escalante
World Wide Web URL: http://www.ericdigests.org/
1996-2/migrant.html

Involving Migrant Families in Education

Describes parent involvement in the education process from the perspective of parents and educators and offers strategies to enhance the experience of schooling for migrant students and their families.

Availability:	All requesters
Suggested Grade:	Teacher Reference
Order Number:	not applicable
Production Date:	2000
Format:	Online Article

Source: Yolanda G. Martinez and Jose A. Velazquez
World Wide Web URL: http://www.ericdigests.org/
2001-3/migrant.htm

Kimbark: Focus On Environmental Education

Kimbark is designed to encourage the teaching of environmental education in schools by showing how a primary school uses classroom study and field work.

Availability:	Schools, libraries, homeschoolers, and nursing homes in Illinois, Indiana, Iowa, Michigan, Minnesota, Missouri, Ohio, and Wisconsin only.
Suggested Grade:	Teacher Reference
Order Number:	218
Format:	VHS videotape
Terms:	Return postage is paid by borrower. Book 10-14 days in advance. Return 7 days after showing. Please provide alternate showing date.

Source: U. S. Fish and Wildlife Service
Region 3, Resource Library
3815 American Boulevard
Bloomington, MN 55425
Fax: 1-612-725-3279
Email Address: judy_geck@fws.gov

Learning and Earning: The Value of Working for Urban Students

Explores this issue.

Availability:	All requesters
Suggested Grade:	Teacher Reference
Order Number:	not applicable
Production Date:	1997
Format:	Online Article

Source: David Stern
World Wide Web URL:
http://www.ericdigests.org/1998-1/value.htm

Let Your Students Take the Lead

Discusses the effectiveness of student-led conferences.

Availability:	All requesters
Suggested Grade:	Teacher Reference
Order Number:	not applicable
Format:	Online Article

Source: Linda Pierce Picciotto
World Wide Web URL:
http://teacher.scholastic.com/professional/classmgmt/
studentslead.htm

Make a Difference: Tips for Teaching Students Who Are Deaf or Hard of Hearing

Addresses the problems faced with teaching mainstreamed deaf or hard of hearing students and presents teaching tips.

Availability:	Schools, libraries, and homeschoolers in the United States who serve the hearing impaired.
Suggested Grade:	Teacher Reference
Order Number:	27748
Production Date:	2000
Format:	Streaming Video
Special Notes:	Also available as live streaming video over the Internet.
Terms:	Sponsor pays all transportation costs. Return one week after receipt. Participation is limited to deaf or hard of hearing Americans, their parents, families, teachers,

Indicates an Internet Resource--just enter the URL and instantly access the FREE teaching aid you need!
All materials listed in this 2010-2011 edition are BRAND NEW!
105

counselors, or others whose use would benefit a deaf or hard of hearing person. Only one person in the audience needs to be hearing impaired. You must register--which is free. These videos are all open-captioned--no special equipment is required for viewing.

**Source: Described and Captioned Media Program
National Association of the Deaf
4211 Church Street Ext.
Roebuck, SC 29376
Phone: 1-800-237-6213
Fax: 1-800-538-5636
World Wide Web URL: http://www.dcmp.org**

Meeting the Educational Needs of Southeast Asian Children

Explains how to meet some of the special needs of these children.

Availability:	All requesters
Suggested Grade:	Teacher Reference
Order Number:	not applicable
Production Date:	1990
Format:	Online Article

**Source: Janine Bempechat and Miya C. Omori
World Wide Web URL:
http://www.ericdigests.org/pre-9218/asian.htm**

Mistakes Educational Leaders Make

Identifies common mistakes so that administrators may avoid them.

Availability:	All requesters
Suggested Grade:	Teacher Reference
Order Number:	not applicable
Production Date:	1998
Format:	Online Article

**Source: Clete Bulach, Winston Pickett, and Diane Boothe
World Wide Web URL:
http://www.ericdigests.org/1999-2/mistakes.htm**

Motivation and Middle School Students

Outlines some suggestions for middle school teachers and administrators for enhancing student motivation at this level.

Availability:	All requesters
Suggested Grade:	Teacher Reference
Languages:	English; Spanish
Order Number:	not applicable
Production Date:	1998
Format:	Online Article

**Source: Lynley Hicks Anderman and Carol Midgley
World Wide Web URL:
http://www.ericdigests.org/1999-1/motivation.html**

Mr. Thackwray's Lab Safety Rules

Thirty-five illustrated safety tips for the science lab.

Availability:	All requesters
Suggested Grade:	6-Adult
Order Number:	not applicable
Format:	Web Site

**Source: Howard Debeck Elementary School
World Wide Web URL:
http://nobel.scas.bcit.ca/debeck_pt/science/safety.htm**

Multiage Grouping and Academic Achievement

Explores this issue.

Availability:	All requesters
Suggested Grade:	Teacher Reference
Languages:	English; Spanish
Order Number:	not applicable
Production Date:	2001
Format:	Online Article

**Source: Susan J. Kinsey
World Wide Web URL:
http://www.ericdigests.org/2001-3/grouping.htm**

Multicultural Science Education: Myths, Legends, and Moon Phases

A sample science lesson plan that illustrates the need and methods useful for teaching Native American students astronomy through the legends that are familiar to them.

Availability:	All requesters
Suggested Grade:	5-8
Order Number:	not applicable
Format:	Online Lesson Plan

**Source: Andrea B. Freed, Ph.D.
World Wide Web URL:
http://www.newhorizons.org/strategies/
multicultural/freed.htm**

NASSP Web Site

Provides a variety of resources for high school principals and other administrators.

Availability:	All requesters
Suggested Grade:	Teacher Reference
Order Number:	not applicable
Format:	Web Site

**Source: National Association of Secondary School Principals
World Wide Web URL:
http://www.principals.org/s_nassp/index.asp**

Outcome-Based Education

Explains and examines this hotly debated issue.

Availability:	All requesters
Suggested Grade:	Teacher Reference
Order Number:	not applicable
Production Date:	1993
Format:	Online Article

**Source: Gwennis McNeir
World Wide Web URL:**
http://cepm.uoregon.edu/publications/digests/digest085.html

Outdoor Experiences for Young Children

Considers the rationale for outdoor experience among young children and the reasons for its decline in popularity.

Availability:	All requesters
Suggested Grade:	Teacher Reference
Order Number:	not applicable

Production Date: 2000
Format: Online Article
Source: Mary S. Rivkin
World Wide Web URL:
http://www.ericdigests.org/2001-3/children.htm

Parent, Family, and Community Involvement in the Middle Grades

Explores this issue in a concise report.

Availability: All requesters
Suggested Grade: Teacher Reference
Order Number: not applicable
Production Date: 1995
Format: Online Article
Source: Barry Rutherford and Shelley H. Billig
World Wide Web URL:
http://www.ericdigests.org/1996-2/parent.html

Perspectives on Charter Schools: A Review for Parents

Offers information on charter schools including discussing how they have been perceived and the success rate of these special schools.

Availability: All requesters
Suggested Grade: Teacher Reference
Languages: English; Spanish
Order Number: not applicable
Production Date: 2001
Format: Online Article
Source: Saran Donahoo
World Wide Web URL:
http://www.ericdigests.org/2002-2/charter.htm

Place-Based Curriculum and Instruction: Outdoor and Environmental Education Approaches

Reviews place-based curriculum and instruction, especially as it relates to outdoor and environmental education, and provides examples of K-12 resources and programs.

Availability: All requesters
Suggested Grade: Teacher Reference
Order Number: not applicable
Production Date: 2000
Format: Online Article
Source: Janice L. Woodhouse and Clifford E. Knapp
World Wide Web URL:
http://www.ericdigests.org/2001-3/place.htm

Poetry and Science Education

Explores the effectiveness of using poetry in the science classroom.

Availability: All requesters
Suggested Grade: Teacher Reference
Order Number: not applicable
Production Date: 2000
Format: Online Article
Source: Davi Walders
World Wide Web URL:
http://www.ericdigests.org/2003-1/poetry.htm

Practitioner Assessment of Conflict Resolution Programs

Discusses this issue.

Availability: All requesters
Suggested Grade: Teacher Reference
Order Number: not applicable
Production Date: 2000
Format: Online Article
Source: Morton Deutsch
World Wide Web URL: http://www.ericdigests.org/
2001-4/conflict.html

Preventing Bullying

Discusses this topic.

Availability: All requesters
Suggested Grade: Teacher Reference
Order Number: not applicable
Production Date: 2002
Format: Online Article
Source: Linda Lumsden
World Wide Web URL:
http://www.ericdigests.org/2003-1/bullying.htm

Principal Mentoring

Examines the nature of mentorships and discusses how these relationships can prepare principals for the next stage of their careers.

Availability: All requesters
Suggested Grade: Teacher Reference
Order Number: not applicable
Production Date: 2001
Format: Online Article
Source: Robert J. Malone
World Wide Web URL:
http://cepm.uoregon.edu/publications/digests/digest149.html

Profiling Students for Violence

Defines profiling, discusses issues raised by profiling students for violence, and describes additional strategies for reducing the risk of violence in schools.

Availability: All requesters
Suggested Grade: Teacher Reference
Order Number: not applicable
Production Date: 2000
Format: Online Article
Source: Linda Lumsden
World Wide Web URL:
http://www.ericdigests.org/2001-3/violence.htm

Project LS: Land Stewardship and Lifestyle Decisions

A curriculum for Iowa specific environmental education for ages 10-adult. Units on prairies, woodlands, wetlands, natural history and heritage.

Availability: Schools, libraries, homeschoolers, and nursing homes in Illinois, Indiana, Iowa, Michigan, Minnesota, Missouri, Ohio, and Wisconsin only.
Suggested Grade: Teacher Reference

 Indicates an Internet Resource--just enter the URL and instantly access the FREE teaching aid you need!
*All materials listed in this 2010-2011 edition are **BRAND NEW!***

107

Order Number: 252
Format: VHS videotape
Special Notes: Includes a teacher's guide.
Terms: Return postage is paid by borrower. Book 10-14 days in advance. Return 7 days after showing. Please provide alternate showing date.

**Source: U. S. Fish and Wildlife Service
Region 3, Resource Library
3815 American Boulevard
Bloomington, MN 55425
Fax: 1-612-725-3279**

Email Address: judy_geck@fws.gov

Recruiting and Retaining Rural School Administrators
Summarizes recent research on this topic.

Availability: All requesters
Suggested Grade: Teacher Reference
Order Number: not applicable
Production Date: 2002
Format: Online Article

**Source: Aimee Howley and Edwina Pendarvis
World Wide Web URL:
http://www.ericdigests.org/2003-4/rural-administrators.html**

Renaissance In Science Teaching
An introduction to the concepts behind the ZEST (Zoos for Effective Science Teaching) teacher training program. ZEST is designed to take the cultural institution beyond the traditional role of providing a simple "enrichment" experience, and makes teacher true collaborators with a science institution in providing a meaningful curriculum for students.

Availability: Schools, libraries, homeschoolers, and nursing homes in Illinois, Indiana, Iowa, Michigan, Minnesota, Missouri, Ohio, and Wisconsin only.
Suggested Grade: Teacher Reference
Order Number: 129
Format: VHS videotape
Terms: Return postage is paid by borrower. Book 10-14 days in advance. Return 7 days after showing. Please provide alternate showing date.

**Source: U. S. Fish and Wildlife Service
Region 3, Resource Library
3815 American Boulevard
Bloomington, MN 55425
Fax: 1-612-725-3279
Email Address: judy_geck@fws.gov**

Report on Violence and Discipline Problems in U. S. Public Schools
A report on this ever-increasing problem.

Availability: All requesters
Suggested Grade: 9-Adult
Order Number: not applicable
Format: Online Article

**Source: National School Safety Center
World Wide Web URL:
http://nces.ed.gov/pubsearch/pubsinfo.asp?pubid=98030**

Restructuring American Schools: The Promise and the Pitfalls
Explores this issue.

Availability: All requesters
Suggested Grade: Teacher Reference
Order Number: not applicable
Production Date: 1989
Format: Online Article

**Source: Lorraine M. McDonnell
World Wide Web URL:
http://www.ericdigests.org/1996-3/work.htm**

Safety in the Laboratory
These safety rules apply to all laboratory activities.

Availability: All requesters
Suggested Grade: 6-Adult
Order Number: not applicable
Format: Web Site

**Source: Gwen Sibert
World Wide Web URL:
http://www.files.chem.vt.edu/RVGS/ACT/
lab/safety_rules.html**

School Calendars
Discusses this topic.

Availability: All requesters
Suggested Grade: Teacher Reference
Order Number: not applicable
Production Date: 2002
Format: Online Article

**Source: Bill Metzker
World Wide Web URL:
http://www.ericdigests.org/2003-2/calendars.html**

School Dropouts: New Information About an Old Problem
Presents statistical information designed to help prevent students from leaving school early.

Availability: All requesters
Suggested Grade: Teacher Reference
Order Number: not applicable
Production Date: 1995
Format: Online Article

**Source: Wendy Schwartz
World Wide Web URL:
http://www.ericdigests.org/1996-2/dropouts.html**

School Practices for Equitable Discipline of African American Students
Discusses this issue.

Availability: All requesters
Suggested Grade: Teacher Reference
Order Number: not applicable
Production Date: 2001

Format: Online Article
Source: Wendy Schwartz
World Wide Web URL:
http://www.ericdigests.org/2002-1/discipline.html

School Safety and the Legal Rights of Students

Presents a brief review of recent Fourth Amendment decisions that affect the rights of students and the parameters of schools' authority to maintain a crime-free environment.

Availability: All requesters
Suggested Grade: Teacher Reference
Order Number: not applicable
Production Date: 1997
Format: Online Article
Source: Dorianne Beyer
World Wide Web URL:
http://www.ericdigests.org/1998-2/safety.htm

School-Site Councils

Discusses school-site councils--easy to mandate, much more difficult to create.

Availability: All requesters
Suggested Grade: Teacher Reference
Order Number: not applicable
Production Date: 1994
Format: Online Article
Source: David Peterson-del Mar
World Wide Web URL:
http://cepm.uoregon.edu/publications/digests/digest089.html

School Size

Discusses school size as an issue related to effective teaching.

Availability: All requesters
Suggested Grade: Teacher Reference
Order Number: not applicable
Production Date: 1997
Format: Online Article
Source: Karen Irmsher
World Wide Web URL:
http://www.ericdigests.org/1998-2/size.htm

Science Lesson Plans that Teach Literacy K-2

Devoted to providing lesson plans and ideas for teachers who want to include science instruction for young children.

Availability: All requesters
Suggested Grade: K-2
Order Number: not applicable
Format: Online Lesson Plans
Source: Kevin Boyle
World Wide Web URL: http://web2.airmail.net/kboyle/

Science Teacher's Guide to TIMSS, A

Discusses the findings of the Third International Mathematics and Science Study.

Availability: All requesters
Suggested Grade: Teacher Reference

Order Number: not applicable
Production Date: 1998
Format: Online Article
Source: Wendy Sherman McCann
World Wide Web URL:
http://www.ericdigests.org/2000-1/science.html

Seven Time-Management Sanity Savers

A former teacher describes a step-by-step process for taking control of time management.

Availability: All requesters
Suggested Grade: Teacher Reference
Order Number: not applicable
Format: Online Article
Source: Beblon Parks
World Wide Web URL:
http://teacher.scholastic.com/professional/classmgmt/
timemanage.htm

Sexual Harassment Interventions

Examines the implications of federal laws covering sexual harassment, the characteristics of company policies and grievance procedures to prevent and report sexual harassment, and program strategies for preventing sexual harassment in schools and workplaces.

Availability: All requesters
Suggested Grade: Teacher Reference
Order Number: not applicable
Production Date: 1999
Format: Online Article
Source: Bettina Lankard Brown
World Wide Web URL:
http://www.ericdigests.org/1999-4/sexual.htm

Standards & Inclusion: Can We Have Both?

Addresses many of the critical issues facing educators who are supporting students with disabilities in inclusive settings.

Availability: Schools, libraries, and homeschoolers in the United States who serve the hearing impaired.
Suggested Grade: Adult
Order Number: 13559
Production Date: 1988
Format: DVD
Special Notes: Also available as live streaming video over the Internet.
Terms: Sponsor pays all transportation costs. Return one week after receipt. Participation is limited to deaf or hard of hearing Americans, their parents, families, teachers, counselors, or others whose use would benefit a deaf or hard of hearing person. Only one person in the audience needs to be hearing impaired. You must register--which is free. These videos are all open-captioned--no special equipment is required for viewing.

Source: Described and Captioned Media Program
National Association of the Deaf
4211 Church Street Ext.
Roebuck, SC 29376
Phone: 1-800-237-6213

 Indicates an Internet Resource--just enter the URL and instantly access the FREE teaching aid you need!
*All materials listed in this 2010-2011 edition are **BRAND NEW!***

109

Fax: 1-800-538-5636
World Wide Web URL: http://www.dcmp.org

Starting Early: Environmental Education During the Early Childhood Years

Discusses the rationale for environmental education during the early years.

Availability: All requesters
Suggested Grade: Teacher Reference
Order Number: not applicable
Production Date: 1996
Format: Online Article
Source: Ruth A. Wilson
World Wide Web URL:
http://www.ericdigests.org/1998-1/early.htm

State English Standards

Do states' current English/language arts reading standards expect what they should? This in-depth report attempts to answer this question.

Availability: Single copies to schools, libraries, and homeschoolers in the United States and Canada. Additional copies are $10.00 each.
Suggested Grade: Teacher Reference
Order Number: order by title
Format: Article
Special Notes: May also be downloaded from the web site.
Source: Thomas B. Fordham Foundation, The
c/o Dunst Fulfillment
106 Competitive Goals Drive
Eldersburg, MD 21784
Phone: 1-888-TBF-7474
World Wide Web URL: http://www.edexcellence.net
Email Address: fordham@dunst.com

Strategies for Improving the Educational Outcomes of Latinas

Presents a range of strategies that schools can employ to promote academic achievement of Latinas.

Availability: All requesters
Suggested Grade: Teacher Reference
Order Number: not applicable
Production Date: 2001
Format: Online Article
Source: Wendy Schwartz
World Wide Web URL:
http://www.ericdigests.org/2002-2/latinas.htm

Student-Led Conferences at the Middle Level

Explores this alternative to the traditional middle level parent-teacher conference.

Availability: All requesters
Suggested Grade: Teacher Reference
Order Number: not applicable
Format: Online Article
Source: Donald G. Hackmann
World Wide Web URL:
http://www.ericdigests.org/1997-4/middle.htm

Student Motivation to Learn

Discusses how to motivate students so that they learn more effectively.

Availability: All requesters
Suggested Grade: Teacher Reference
Order Number: not applicable
Production Date: 1994
Format: Online Article
Source: Linda Lumsden
World Wide Web URL:
http://www.ericdigests.org/1995-1/learn.htm

Teacher Files

Resources, ideas, activities, lessons plans, and more for teachers.

Availability: All requesters
Suggested Grade: All ages
Order Number: not applicable
Format: Web Site
Source: Shayni Tokarczyk
World Wide Web URL:
http://www.teacherfiles.com/http://www.teacherfiles.com/

Teaching About Societal Issues in Science Classrooms

Discusses this issue.

Availability: All requesters
Suggested Grade: Teacher Reference
Order Number: not applicable
Production Date: 1997
Format: Online Article
Source: Wendy Sherman McCann
World Wide Web URL:
http://www.ericdigests.org/2000-1/societal.html

Teaching Science in the Field

Explains how to successfully take students "outside" to learn science.

Availability: All requesters
Suggested Grade: Teacher Reference
Order Number: not applicable
Production Date: 1996
Format: Online Article
Source: Carol Landis
World Wide Web URL:
http://www.ericdigests.org/1998-1/field.htm

Tellecollaborate!

Designed to encourage telecollaboration among educators and students around the world.

Availability: All requesters
Suggested Grade: Teacher Reference
Order Number: not applicable
Format: Web Site
Source: Nancy Schubert
World Wide Web URL: http://nschubert.home.mchsi.com/

Thirteen Ed Online

A web service for K-12 teachers that offers lesson plans for core curriculum topics and lots more.

Availability: All requesters
Suggested Grade: Teacher Reference
Order Number: not applicable
Format: Web Site

Source: Thirteen Ed Online
World Wide Web URL: http://www.thirteen.org/edonline/

TIMSS: What Have We Learned About Math and Science Teaching?

Attempts to answer this question.

Availability: All requesters
Suggested Grade: Teacher Reference
Order Number: not applicable
Production Date: 2000
Format: Online Article

Source: Beth D. Greene, Marlena Herman and David L. Haury
World Wide Web URL:
http://www.ericdigests.org/2003-1/timss.htm

Underachievement Among Gifted Minority Students: Problems and Promises

Provides a basic overview, plus pertinent references, on this topic.

Availability: All requesters
Suggested Grade: Teacher Reference
Order Number: not applicable
Production Date: 1997
Format: Online Article

Source: Donna Y. Ford and Antoinette Thomas
World Wide Web URL:
http://www.ericdigests.org/1998-1/gifted.htm

Uniforms and Dress-Code Policies

Discusses why some schools are changing their dress-code policies, outlines issues raised by proponents and opponents, looks at legal considerations, touches upon research findings, and offers some suggestions from students about other ways to promote safety in schools.

Availability: All requesters
Suggested Grade: Teacher Reference
Order Number: not applicable
Production Date: 2001
Format: Online Article

Source: Linda Lumsden
World Wide Web URL:
http://www.ericdigests.org/2002-1/uniforms.html

What's Right with Schools

Highlights some data that casts the performance of schools in a more favorable light than they currently seem to be getting.

Availability: All requesters
Suggested Grade: Teacher Reference
Order Number: not applicable
Production Date: 1995
Format: Online Article

Source: Jayne Freeman
World Wide Web URL:
https://scholarsbank.uoregon.edu/xmlui/bitstream/handle/
1794/3314/digest093.pdf?sequence=1

Working with Culturally & Linguistically Diverse Families

Examines how educators can effectively work with families of differing backgrounds.

Availability: All requesters
Suggested Grade: Teacher Reference
Order Number: not applicable
Production Date: 2001
Format: Online Article

Source: Deborah A. Bruns and Robert M. Corso
World Wide Web URL:
http://ceep.crc.uiuc.edu/eecearchive/digests/
2001/bruns01.html

Working with Shy or Withdrawn Students

Explores this issue in a concise report.

Availability: All requesters
Suggested Grade: Teacher Reference
Order Number: not applicable
Production Date: 1996
Format: Online Article

Source: Jere Brophy
World Wide Web URL:
http://www.ericdigests.org/1997-3/shy.html

Work Teams in Schools

Discusses the application of work teams in schools.

Availability: All requesters
Suggested Grade: Teacher Reference
Order Number: not applicable
Production Date: 1996
Format: Online Article

Source: Lori Jo Oswald
World Wide Web URL:
http://www.ericdigests.org/1996-3/work.htm

World In Our Backyard, A

Shows the beauty of wetlands and explains how teachers can convey the need to conserve these lands.

Availability: Schools, libraries, and homeschoolers in Connecticut, Maine, Massachusetts, New Hampshire, Rhode Island, and Vermont.
Suggested Grade: 4-12
Order Number: VID 101
Production Date: 1993
Format: VHS videotape
Terms: Borrower pays return postage. Return within three weeks of receipt. If the tape you request is available, it will be mailed within 5 business days. If not, you will be notified that this video is already out on loan. No more than three titles may be borrowed by one requestor at a time. No reservations for a specific date will be accepted. It is most efficient to order via the web site.

Indicates an Internet Resource--just enter the URL and instantly access the FREE teaching aid you need!
*All materials listed in this 2010-2011 edition are **BRAND NEW!***

Source: U. S. Environmental Protection Agency, Region 1
Customer Service Center
One Congress Street, Suite 1100
Boston, MA   02214
World Wide Web URL:
http://yosemite.epa.gov/r1/videolen.nsf/

YES I Can! Science

Provides teacher resources, classroom activities, and lesson plans that support the Canadian science curriculum.

Availability: All requesters
Suggested Grade: K-12
Languages: English; French
Order Number: not applicable
Format: Web Site

Source: York University
World Wide Web URL: http://www.yesican-science.ca/

You Can Handle Them All

This web site describes 117 different behaviors and examines the effects of these behaviors and others. Advice is offered about good and bad ways to go about changing the behavior.

Availability: All requesters
Suggested Grade: Teacher Reference
Order Number: not applicable
Format: Web Site

Source: Leadership Lane
World Wide Web URL:
http://www.disciplinehelp.com/teacher/list.cfm?cause=All

-A-

-B-

TITLE INDEX

-X-Y-Z-

SUBJECT INDEX

SUBJECT INDEX

SUBJECT INDEX

SUBJECT INDEX

SUBJECT INDEX

SUBJECT INDEX

SUBJECT INDEX

SUBJECT INDEX

The SOURCE INDEX is an alphabetical list of the organizations from which the materials listed in the EDUCATORS GUIDE TO FREE SCIENCE MATERIALS may be obtained. There are 380 sources listed in this Fifty-First Edition of the GUIDE, **of which 340 are new**. The numbers following each listing are the page numbers on which the materials from each source are annotated in the body of the GUIDE.

When requesting materials via mail or fax, please use a letter of request similar to the sample shown in the front part of the GUIDE. When requesting via telephone, please have the name of the material you desire in front of you (along with the order number if necessary). Please read each listing carefully to be certain that the material you are requesting is available via the method through which you choose to order.

Bold type indicates a source that is new in the 2010-2011 edition. Complete addresses for each source are found following the description of the material in the body of the GUIDE.

SOURCE INDEX

SOURCE INDEX

SOURCE INDEX

SOURCE INDEX

**Educators
Progress
Service,
Inc.**

**214 Center Street
Randolph, Wisconsin 53956
920/326-3126
www.freeteachingaids.com**